SUSTAINABLE ASSET MANAGEMENT

HOW TO ORDER THIS BOOK

BY PHONE: 717-290-1660, 9AM–5PM Eastern Time

BY FAX: 717-509-6100

BY MAIL: Order Department
DEStech Publications, Inc.
439 North Duke Street
Lancaster, PA 17602, U.S.A.

BY CREDIT CARD: VISA, MasterCard, American Express

BY WWW SITE: http://www.destechpub.com

SUSTAINABLE ASSET MANAGEMENT

Linking assets, people,
and processes for results

Roopchan Lutchman

DE*Stech* Publications, Inc.

Sustainable Asset Management

DEStech Publications, Inc.
439 North Duke Street
Lancaster, Pennsylvania 17602 U.S.A.

Printed in the United States of America
10 9 8 7 6 5 4 3 2

Entry under main title:
    Sustainable Asset Management: Linking Assets, People, and Processes for Results

A DEStech Publications book
Bibliography: p.
Includes index p. 253

Library of Congress Catalog Card No. 2006922602
ISBN: 1-932078-47-9
ISBN13: 978-1-932078-47-3

Asset management is a popular term today, but it is poorly understood. Currently, strategic and sustainable asset management programs could benefit many major industries, as well as utilities. Repair costs for underground infrastructure defects in the United States alone are estimated to be in the billions of dollars. In many cases, there is significant investment in new infrastructure without any attention paid to correcting problems that cause deterioration. Most of the past two decades have focused on improvements in operations and work management business processes. In general, the Operations and Maintenance phase of the asset lifecycle is the main focus of day-to-day activities. Often, the maintenance of assets is reactive—with resulting poor asset reliability. All phases of the asset lifecycle are unwittingly managed in silos (a focus on individual phases without out concern for the impact or needs of other phases). Indeed many involved in the asset lifecycle are unaware of the various phases of the asset lifecycle. The unpopularity of engineers with operations and maintenance staff is a direct result of this siloed view of the asset. When one considers that design and creation of a typical asset takes 2 to 3 years and operations and maintenance can go on for 60–100 years, it is clear that shortcomings in the design and construction phase can have huge undesired consequences for later phases of the asset life.

Today, many companies are faced with a blitz of solutions to their perceived needs. Many have undertaken or are in the process of implementing the following programs: Strategic Planning, Business Optimization, Total Quality Management, Kaizen, Total Productive Maintenance, Performance Management, Succession Planning, Six-Sigma, Lean manufacturing, Computerized Work Management Systems and Other

Technology Solutions, Empowered Teams, Organizational Effectiveness and the list goes on. These initiatives can yield real and sustainable results if the focus is on the bottom line: *maximizing asset performance and reliability while minimizing overall cost of ownership.* Unfortunately, most of these programs are un-coordinated and seldom provide the return on the investment. In fact in many companies, employees have become so frustrated with change programs they get worried when managers go off on conferences expecting to see them initiate a new program on their return.

There are many business drivers for change in the various industries today that will result in the demise of companies if they do not understand what they are facing and respond quickly and appropriately to these changes. These include:

- Higher customer expectations
- Large infrastructure condition gap
- Globalization—competition from low-cost producers
- Need to be competitive—lower O&M costs
- Limited funds to finance asset programs
- Need to meet regulations—(USA—GASB 34, CMOM, Canada—Bills 175, 195, Kyoto Accord)
- Privatization threats
- Baby boomer effect (looming major retirement crisis) and potential loss of asset related corporate knowledge
- Growth in population, market share etc.
- More advanced technology/designs available—obsolete assets
- Need for sustainability (manage the triple bottom line—social, economic and environmental)

It is not adequate to react to these business drivers by focusing on business processes or assets or people-related solutions. The solution must embody all three of these elements and must embrace all the drivers relevant to your type of industry and operating context.

Few books deal with asset management in a practical and meaningful way. Most publications focus on the symptoms rather than the root causes of the asset management problems facing industries today. The approach to asset management proposed in this volume is one that ensures sustainability in all of the three key areas: *assets, people, and processes.* This book will help you provide realistic answers to the following questions and give you practical suggestions to develop solutions if you discover you are not operating a competitive and high-performance organization:

1. What assets do you own?
2. Which are the critical ones?
3. What is the lifecycle cost data associated with each asset?
4. What is the current condition of your assets?
5. What is their deterioration rate?
6. What are the market, book and replacement values of the asset?
7. How are you organized to take care of them—do you have the right skills and team arrangements, are you proactively developing the new skills needed to meet the changing demands of the business environment?
8. What are your recruitment, retention, and succession-planning strategies?
9. What business processes do you need to maximize reliability and performance and reduce costs?
10. Are you leveraging the appropriate technology assets in support of asset management—hardware, business software, automation and control?
11. Do you have an integrated technology asset solution and how do you manage it?
12. How do you manage all knowledge around the assets—capture, store, continuously update and share this knowledge?
13. Do you have a 20-year capital program that provides short, medium and long-term plans for asset modifications, upgrade or replacements?
14. Is the capital program for asset related projects driven by economic parameters such as Net Present Value (NPV), Rate of Return on Investment (ROI), and Payback Period?
15. Do you have standards for asset-related processes around each phase of the asset lifecycle?

My approach to the subject is based on experiences within many industries, including lifecycle management, design and implementation of asset management programs with organization design, and enabling technologies. Sustainable asset management provides a practical and logical approach to understanding asset management, developing industry-specific practices, a high-performance organization, and enabling technologies. The resulting asset management program will allow your company to deal with current asset management problems and help you establish a realistic asset management business process. The information provided is both strategic and tactical and is designed for senior management, middle management, and frontline staff. The methodologies and solutions to problems are practical, and staff can readily absorb them. The graphics are simple and provide value in explaining concepts and making them easy to remember. The book is intended to help managers grasp the overall picture. Co-ordination requirements around the asset lifecycle will assist employees in operations and maintenance.

Finally, this book has instructional value for students of asset management, as well as operations and maintenance. Its chapters are organized to correspond to the syllabus of asset management courses in technical schools and universities.

ACKNOWLEDGEMENTS

To the many people who have influenced my thoughts and ideas and have encouraged me to write this book so that others can benefit. I would also like to thank my wife and children for giving me the support I needed to make this book a reality. Special recognition goes to my colleague Mohsen Mortada for encouraging and reassuring me that my ideas were valuable and worthy of a book on asset management. Finally, I wish to thank the many asset management practitioners who have willingly shared their ideas and experiences during my career.

CHAPTER 1

Introduction to Asset Management

Until recently (3–5 years ago) asset management was relatively unknown in North America. It has been confused with the term used to describe how investment bankers manage financial assets. Many people in the operations and maintenance area interpret asset management to mean maintenance (or work) management. Very few companies understand the difference between asset and maintenance management. The most advanced practitioners of asset management are water, wastewater and public works utilities in New Zealand and Australia. They have set the general direction and standards for asset management in these industries. Many manufacturing, process and heavy equipment industries (e.g., mining) have yet to organize themselves around the asset lifecycle and struggle with the health care of their assets. Asset management is a relatively new concept that incorporates existing asset-related practices and adds new concepts aimed at helping companies focus on the triple bottom line instead of the financial bottom line alone.

OVERVIEW OF ASSET MANAGEMENT

An asset is any entity that can be used to produce a good, product or a service to meet the needs of a client or customer. Usually, a customer or client is willing to pay directly for this service or indirectly through taxes paid to cities or the government. Assets fall into three major categories: discrete assets (e.g., pumps, packaging lines, buildings, drag lines, haul trucks, planes, vehicles and computers), linear or continuous assets (water pipes, sewers, roads, land, electric transmission lines), and virtual as-

1

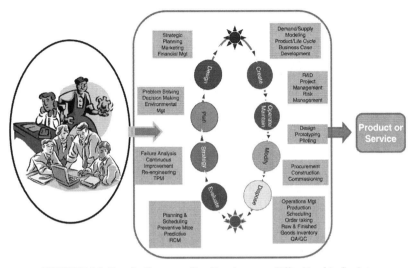

FIGURE 1.1 *People Create and/or Use Assets to Fill a Need in Society.*

sets (e.g. software). All assets go through similar lifecycle phases, starting from preliminary "Needs" and ending at the final phase of being "Decommissioned" or "Replaced." Asset Management is the management of the collection of practices associated with each lifecycle phase. Companies use people to perform work at each phase of the asset lifecycle with the ultimate goal of creating value through a product or service required to satisfy a need in society (Figure 1.1). Asset management is the glue that ensures everything is effectively managed to ensure that maximum value is created over the asset lifecycle. Asset management must have clear strategies and tactics for each strategy in order for this business process to be effective and value added to the company.

   Asset Management is a critical link in balancing product or service delivery costs to achieve and sustain customer satisfaction. It is one of the most important and yet neglected practices associated with developing a competitive organization. Recent trends of higher customer expectations for product performance and reliability, service delivery, more stringent quality requirements (enforced by stricter regulations), limited sources of funding for asset upgrades or replacement, and increased demands for accountability have made Asset Management a current and important business practice. Unfortunately, the response to the drivers has been very reactive with major efforts focused on containing immediate problems, normally pertaining to only one or two lifecycle phases. There is definitely a major need for a strategic asset management that involves all organization units playing the right role in the different phases of the asset's lifecycle and supported by the appropriate integrated technology solution. This book is intended to help those charged with the overall management of the asset lifecycle or individual phases to approach the task in a systematic and practical manner, focusing on the various best in class asset management practices, the most suitable supporting organization components, and the enabling technologies required to drive strategic asset management.

THE ASSET LIFECYCLE

Understanding the Asset Lifecycle (Figure 1.2) is critical to effective asset management. All assets go through an eight-stage process during its life. There are different requirements for asset management at each of these stages. The following discussion gives a brief overview of the asset lifecycle (this will be covered in more detail in Chapter 2).

Stage 1—Evaluate and Identify a Need

Identifying a need is the most important stage of the asset lifecycle. Making the wrong decision at this stage can have major consequences

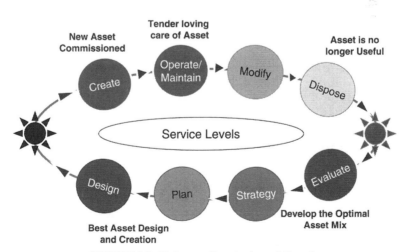

FIGURE 1.2 *Understanding the Asset Lifecycle.*

over the rest of the life of the asset. Imagine the impact for assets with lives of 75–100 years! Identifying a need involves an analysis of changing client demands, a critical review of the ability of the current asset mix to meet these demands (through improved maintenance, upgrade or modification), and the impact of technological obsolescence. Once the need for a new asset is determined, formal planning is necessary.

Stage 2—Develop an Asset Strategy

Before meaningful planning can take place for a new asset, it is important to determine the overall asset strategy. This requires a high-level understanding of the purpose of the asset (e.g., need to be fulfilled), proposed lifespan, first cut of the business case, type of ownership (company owned, leased, rental, or DBO (design, build and operate). A choice in any of he above categories will influence what happens in the subsequent stages of the asset lifecycle. The decision to expand the fleet in a company by purchasing additional cars and truck will dictate the need for a maintenance strategy, which in turn requires additional maintenance trades, inventory items, and possibly expansion of the maintenance shop. The decision to lease additional vehicles with responsibility for maintenance being the responsibility of the dealer creates a completely new strategy for maintenance. In this case it may only be necessary to increase the supervisory ranks to help manage the lease contract.

Stage 3—Plan

The level of planning is dictated by the criticality and investment cost associated with the asset. At this stage it is advisable to conduct a proper economic analysis to support a winning proposal for investment funds (the net present value [NPV] concept is the preferred economic tool). If the proposal is for replacement of an existing asset (at the end of its life), proper documentation is necessary to support the recommendation to replace the asset. O&M staff must work closely with engineering and finance personnel to prepare a proposal that can compete for scarce funds. In many cases a project with great NPV is just the start of the planning process; securing the funding from bondholders or raising rates to finance the project may be the biggest undertaking or challenge at this stage.

Stage 4—Design

Approval to proceed with a new asset sets the stage for the design process. The rule of thumb at this stage it is to involve the O&M staff, if you want to create an asset that will serve the needs of the end user. Many effective design engineers credit their success to the practical ideas and suggestions they receive from O&M staff. Designers are very aware that their brief activity (3–6 months) sets the stage for operating and maintaining an asset for the rest of its life (over 75 years in some cases). Incorporation of the latest technological advances with due consideration for safety and environmental needs and compatibility with the existing asset base are key inputs into the design stage. Design should have the lowest overall cost of ownership as its key objective.

Stage 5: Create—Procure/Build/Commission

Good project management, with a focus on time, scope, money and impact on the existing operations, is important in the successful creation of an asset. Involvement of O&M staff at key points of the project allows for the critical knowledge transfer needed to operate and maintain the asset and also provides needed quality control during construction. At this stage all the necessary documentation to support operations and maintenance should be provided electronically to populate the Computerized Work Management System (CWMS), Geographical Information System (GIS), Supervisory Control and Data Acquisition (SCADA), and Asset Management Systems. In the past the commissioning process has served as the formal handover of the asset (or project) to the owners. O&M personnel have always interpreted it as the event that allows engineering to obtain a signature and "wash their hands" of the project. The commissioning stage should be taken more seriously and be viewed as an opportunity to provide all the baseline information O&M needs, along with the asset in its original condition. It is also a great opportunity for engineering to confirm their ongoing support for O&M and to seek feedback that could enhance their design and implementation procedures.

Stage 6—*Operate* and Maintain

Operation is the longest stage of the asset lifecycle varying in time from one year for low-cost disposable assets (e.g., small chemical pumps) to over 50 years for water pumps, water mains, or sewer lines. Manufacturing, automotive and airline assets have a much shorter life span but a similar high ratio of operations time to the rest of the asset's life. Knowing every aspect of the asset, knowing how to operate it safely at its designed and required performance levels, and how to ensure that it meets environmental standards are important for providing a quality product or service. Good operations management is the cornerstone of optimal asset performance, reliability, and cost effectiveness. This cannot be done in isolation. Rather, it requires a lasting partnership with the maintenance group.

Maintain

Operation and maintenance of the asset are parallel phases of the lifecycle, which starts at commissioning and ends at the disposal or replacement stage. It is essential that the right maintenance tactics are developed to achieve cost-effective performance and optimal reliability of the asset. The appropriate mix of best-practice concepts such as Optimized Maintenance, Reliability Centered Maintenance, Predictive/Condition-Based Maintenance, and Total Productive Maintenance should be used to support an effective work management process. Data such as cost, work history and asset condition should be recorded on a regular basis during the course of doing work, so that asset deterioration curves can be plotted and economic analyses carried out to determine if the asset is doing its job in a cost-effective manner. The output from these analyses will determine whether the asset should be modified or decommissioned and/or replaced and will be instrumental in driving the capital improvement program of the company.

Stage 7—Modify

Ongoing monitoring of asset performance in line with desired performance or projected changes in demand may dictate the need to modify the asset. In addition, there may be safety or environmental problems requiring upgrade or modifications to ensure that the company can continue using the asset. Any projects that are identified in this area should also be supported by a proper economic evaluation. Modifications must follow sound engineering design standards and should, at a minimum, have input from operations, maintenance, and engineering. The asset database should be updated to reflect all changes (technical specifications, operating and maintenance manuals, and financial information) to the asset and be made available to relevant personnel.

Stage 8—Decommission (Dispose/Replace)

Decommissioning ends the asset lifecycle and in most cases is closely tied with the creation of a new asset as the old one is decommissioned, "moth-balled," or removed from a site. When decommissioning is related to reduced demand for service or product, then the key focus is to ensure that the asset is left in a state that ensures it is protected from degradation and cannibalization for spares. It must be properly secured. In the event that the asset must be salvaged, safety and environmental considerations should be incorporated into the salvage process. As in the modification stage, the asset database should be updated to reflect these changes.

It is important to note that there is a financial requirement to track the value of the asset from the creation stage to the disposal stage. The concepts of market and book value (based on accepted depreciation rules) should be applied in determining any asset-related financial information. A detailed review of the asset lifecycle with supporting examples is provided in Chapter 2.

CHALLENGES FACING ASSET MANAGEMENT IN INDUSTRY TODAY

Most people go through the ritual budget dance each year laboring for days on end to develop proposals for investment in existing and new assets. In many cases, there are limited funds to go around—any dollars used to fund new assets means fewer dollars to fund other projects. For a number of years, the easy solution has been to invest smaller sums to keep old equipment and infrastructure limping along. As we all know, this is a very shortsighted approach, and there are many examples of people spending enormous figures over a period of time on old, obsolete, technologically inferior assets when the right decision in the past on a new asset would have yielded a much lower cost of ownership, better products or service delivery, happier employees, and more satisfied customers. This questionable practice is catching up with many industries, especially in the public arena. The Water Infrastructure Network has suggested there is a gap of $23 billion dollars (US) between capital needs and current spending over the next 20 years to bring the US water and wastewater infrastructure to an acceptable level. Even if this level of funding were possible, the underlying reasons for the deterioration would probably still exist. Bridges, roads, and other public works infrastructure are experiencing the same fate. The average age of vehicle fleets in many cities has moved from 6 years to 12 years. Many manufacturing companies are unable to modernize or retool their production lines and live with consequent downtime, safety, and quality issues. Most airlines are struggling to stay in business and balance the need for younger fleets. The solution requires a focus on upgrading assets together with the implementation of an asset management program that will sustain cost-effective asset reliability and performance. Current drivers for strategic asset management include:

- Reduced funding for O&M upgrades, modifications, or replacements.
- Increased growth and the need to meet new output levels by creating or acquiring new assets.
- Higher customer expectations (value for money)—higher quality service or products.
- Pressure to maintain or reduce product prices or rates charged to clients.
- More stringent regulations:
  —Water, wastewater industry—US Government Accounting and Standards Board (GASB 34), Capacity Management Operations & Maintenance (CMOM), Canada (Sustainable Water and Sewage Systems Act and Safe Drinking Water Act)
  —Electricity generation, iron and steel—Kyoto Accord (stringent limits on environmental contamination).
  —Oil and Gas—pollution limits set by the environmental protection agencies of various countries.
- Aging infrastructure, with many assets beyond or close to the end of their economic life.
- More advanced technology/designs available—obsolete assets.
- Privatization—need to write asset management standards into contracts and protect the client's investment.
- Increased competition to provide the same product or services.
- Globalization—cheaper supply of labor, less stringent regulations.
- Higher energy costs (electrical and heating).
- Changing workforce—baby boomer retirement, diversity, wellness issues

A full discussion of the asset management challenges facing different industries and the unique drivers for change is given in Chapter 3.

BENEFITS OF IMPLEMENTING AN ASSET MANAGEMENT PROGRAM

Many reasons have been given for asset management. Still the question can be raised: do real benefits accrue as a result of developing and implementing a sustainable asset management program. In fact, it is important to quantify both tangible and intangible benefits to build the case for an asset management program. An effective asset management program will provide consistency in execution of all activities associated with the asset lifecycle of the asset. The following are major benefits of implementing an asset management program:

- Minimum overall cost of ownership for the asset—through cost-effective asset creation, preservation and replacement.
- Keeps the organization focused on the objective of customer satisfaction through effective service and product delivery.
- Creates ownership and buy-in through involvement of staff that ensures there is always a business focus on creating new assets, preserving or replacing current assets.
- Incorporates asset related performance measures into the overall performance management program provides on going information on whether the asset management practice is cost effective and current at all times.
- Eliminates funding crisis situations (requiring major injection of funds to upgrade and replace assets that can no longer meet performance standards).
- Provides a vehicle for corporate knowledge retention and sharing as it relates to assets
- Improves overall organizational effectiveness (through better coordination and communication) with common goals around the asset throughout its lifecycle.
- Improves safety and environmental record (less accidents and environmental issues.
- Protects the company from litigation in the event of safety issues by clearly demonstrating all possible measures were taken to ensure safety in the operation of the asset.

Identifying the tangible and intangible benefits of an effective asset management relevant to a given industry is key to building a business case for developing and implementing a sustainable asset management program. Chapter 4 provides a step-by-step guide for developing a convincing and sound business case for asset management.

ASSET MANAGEMENT IS A PART OF AN INTEGRATED BUSINESS MODEL

The recent attention given to Asset Management, as a result of the above drivers, has caused a scramble among companies to implement a suitable program. In most cases this has been to the detriment of other initiatives designed to make the company competitive. In many situations, implementing an asset management program is interpreted to mean: conducting a condition audit of the current infrastructure or asset mix, seeking appropriate funding to have replacements or upgrades done, or implementing a CWMS. Generally we find that the business process and people requirements for Asset Management are not fully evaluated and developed. It is extremely important that these components are considered alongside analysis of an asset's condition. Development of an asset management practice requires a full understanding of how work and operations management impact management of assets throughout an asset's lifecycle. In addition, it requires optimization of resources (people, tools, equipment, materials, energy, chemicals etc.) and management of performance at all stages of the asset lifecycle to achieve customer satisfaction. Figure 1.3 shows how the asset infrastructure mix can vary with changes in customer demand. Changes in the level of service or product demand by customers will require changes in the asset mix and the associated resources needed to be effective at Asset, Work and Operations Management. Chapter 5 takes the reader through the

Demand and Supply Modeling Defines the Asset Mix

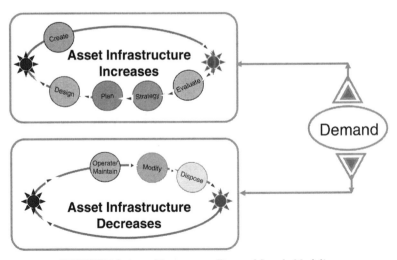

FIGURE 1.3 *Asset Management Demand Supply Modeling.*

process of developing a sustainable asset management framework applicable to any industry.

Effective asset management must be based on practices that are easily implemented, cost effective, and sustainable in the long run. The best-in-class practices fall into two categories—general practices that apply to the entire asset lifecycle of the asset and specific practices relevant to unique lifecycle phases. All leading practices can be visualized as a continuum where the low end of the scale asset management behavior can be categorized as "innocence" and the high end as "excellence." A good understanding of best-in-class practices is fundamental to transforming ineffective business processes into lean and value-added ones necessary for a highly competitive and admired operation. Chapter 6 explores leading practices in the two categories identified and makes the link between asset management and sustainability/triple bottom line (economic, social and environmental). Suitable asset management standards by asset class and type are necessary for ensuring consistency in asset-related activities throughout an asset's lifecycle (these are discussed in Chapter 9). In addition, a redesign of business practices not only yields smarter ways of working but also identifies supporting roles and responsibilities and the enabling technologies needed to complete the asset management framework.

DESIGNING A HIGH PERFORMANCE ORGANIZATION TO SUPPORT ASSET MANAGEMENT

Everyone has a role to play if asset management is going to be effective. Achieving proper coordination of asset management activities among all groups presents a major challenge. This can be resolved by the development of a common vision for asset management, which is shared by everyone. Goals and objectives must be clearly defined, with appropriate responsibility assigned to different groups and individuals. In some cases, this might be reflected in Service Level Agreements (SLA), which identify what each group has to provide for others to support asset management, along with mutually agreed performance measures and targets. Some companies have assigned the responsibility for the design, implementation, and overall coordination of an asset management program to an asset manager. This role requires extensive knowledge of the various assets as it relates to each aspect of their lifecycle, excellent leadership and interpersonal skills, together with an aptitude for juggling many tasks at the same time. The key to success in asset management is the coordination of all types of work across the various phases of the asset's lifecycle. Traditional organization designs have encouraged organizational silos with consequential inefficiencies in the way assets are managed. For example, when engineers do not communicate with operations and maintenance staff the resulting designs can miss basic maintainability and operations needs (resulting in the popular anti-engineer views at the shop floor level). Redesign of relevant practices will yield the desired roles and responsibilities necessary to effectively support asset management. These roles and responsibilities can be combined with organization design principles to develop the different organizational levels (*visioning, strategic, tactical, operational, and task*) and supporting job descriptions. The key to successful coordination of an Asset Management program is good communication, supported by quality information made easily available through an enabling technology solution. The resulting high-performance organization enables effective work communication in all areas of asset management. Chapter 7 provides guidelines for making the relevant organizational changes needed to support an asset management program.

ASSET MANAGEMENT AND ENABLING TECHNOLOGIES

An effective asset management program depends on the collection, screening, and evaluation of vast amounts of data, in order to make decisions related to the asset at various stages in its lifecycle. This data can be financial, work-, operations-, maintenance- and condition-related (e.g., data needed to plot deterioration curves). Figure 1.4—Integrated Technology Supports Asset Management, shows that there are two core business applications necessary for effective asset management: Computerized Work Management System (CWMS) and an Asset Management System (AMS). The integrated technology solution requires interfaces and links between the CWMS and other business applications such as Financials and Administrations System (FAS), Geographical Information System (GIS), SCADA/Process Control, Pavement Management Systems, Predictive Maintenance Systems (PdM), Closed Circuit Television (CCTV), in order to do effective work management on the asset. Data captured in this process can then feed an asset management system for plotting of deterioration curves, economic modeling and development of the capital project plans that will then be executed in the CWMS. This data will also be the source for creating the necessary reports to manage performance and provide proof of regulatory compliance (e.g., GASB 34 reports). The asset management system should also be able to provide an integrated view of assets. For example, in the public works environment one should be able to see the condition of the pavement, water line, sewer line for a particular segment of street. Any im-

Integrated Technology Supports Asset Management

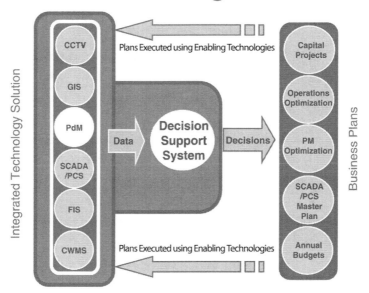

FIGURE 1.4 *Integrated Technology Supports Asset Management.*

provement plan for the overall integrated asset should be taken into account when modeling is carried out. Major challenges that must be resolved in the development of an enabling integrated technology solution are: maintaining the integrity of the asset record especially where it is shared by many different systems, developing a common asset numbering system, and achieving an appropriate balance for real time, near real time and batch data transfer. A complete overview of the design and development of an integrated technology solution to enable asset management is provided in Chapter 8.

DESIGN AND IMPLEMENTATION OF A SUSTAINABLE ASSET MANAGEMENT PROGRAM

Essentially, designing and implementing sustainable asset management is a change process that requires critiquing and identifying business opportunities, defining improvement tactics, and implementing measures to sustain new asset management behaviors. It can be visualized as "unfreezing" the organization, making desired changes and then "refreezing" the organization to sustain the new culture and behaviors. A step-by-step transformation methodology is discussed and used as the roadmap for design of a program, development of funding strategies, and implementation of the program. As with any change process, this process has to be properly managed to ensure it is done in a manner that minimizes any negative impact on business activities and ensures ownership and buy-in at all levels. Chapters 10, 11 and 12 provide full details on these important topics.

MANAGE PERFORMANCE TO ACHIEVE AND SUSTAIN EFFECTIVE ASSET MANAGEMENT

Sustaining high-caliber performance in asset management requires that performance be closely tracked against mutually agreed and realistic targets. There must be a clear understanding of what should be measured and tracked, how often the measures should be done, and how to recognize and act on deviations that are unacceptable. Asset management measures must also fit in into the overall performance management framework for your company and must make sense. An effective asset management practice ensures optimal performance by focusing on:

- Making the most appropriate design choices for creating a new asset, based on the full cost of ownership, funding strategies, operations and maintenance needs.
- Involvement of O&M staff in the construction and ownership phase to maximize knowledge transfer.
- Asset preservation through continuously striving to maximize asset reliability and at the same time meeting the desired performance standards in a cost-effective manner using the right mix of maintenance philosophies.
- Asset upgrade, modification and/or replace assets based on sound economic criteria.
- Asset decommissioning or disposal in a manner that maximizes salvage value and at the same time conforms to environmental regulations.

A good Asset Management program should provide measures for the various categories of assets in the following areas:

- Asset Financial Indicators:
  —Return On Net Asset (RONA).
  —Book and Market Values.

- Asset Performance Indicators.
- Safety and the Environment.
  —No of incidences of environmental regulatory violations per year.
  —No incidences of safety violations per year.
- Asset creation measures.

A detailed discussion on asset management performance is provided in Chapter 13.

CONCLUSION

Asset Management is a critical link in balancing overall product or service delivery cost of ownership to achieve and sustain customer satisfaction. It cannot be considered in isolation, since it is an integral part of the overall business model. Current drivers for asset management make asset management one of the most critical issues on the minds of many leaders today. Many are overwhelmed by the enormity of the task facing them and are concerned about their company's ability to design, implement, and sustain an effective asset management program. The situation becomes even more complicated when implementation must be considered together with other major ongoing initiatives (plant upgrades, new technology, competitiveness programs etc.). This book provides practical guidance on the overall asset management concept, its relation to the business model, its benefits, performance measures, and an implementation approach for those contemplating such a program.

CHAPTER 2

Assets and the Asset Lifecycle

ASSETS AND THE ASSET LIFECYCLE

Asset is a term used to describe many things. In the banking and investment sector, assets refer to financial holdings, cash, bonds and stock. Some people refer to their physical attributes as their assets. This book is about the assets that create products and services, which in turn allow citizens to secure quality of life, happiness, and general well being. Such assets include water and wastewater systems, roads, vehicles, planes, trains, ships, plants and machinery, parks and recreational areas, weapons, hardware, and software. Many assets are designed to produce other assets (e.g., robots used in the production of automobiles).

Definition of an Asset

An asset is any entity that can be used to produce a product or a service to meet the needs of a client or customer.

Essentially, Assets Fall into 3 Main Categories—Discrete, Linear and Intangible (They can also be Broken Down into Subcategories Unique to the Design or Service)

Discrete assets—refer to assets that have clear and unique boundaries and can be identified using the five senses. Discrete assets are fixed (pumps, buildings, trees, traffic lights, reservoirs) or mobile (planes, trains, vehicles). Subcategories for discrete assets are based on the type of asset. For example, subcategories of pumps are: centrifugal, reciprocating, diaphragm, progressive cavity, and gear.

Linear assets—are usually continuous with one or more undefined boundaries and again can be identified using the five senses. Linear assets are typically fixed (underground water and sewer lines, roads, drains, electric lines, rails, park areas). Subcategories of linear assets may be based on the material used in the asset. For example, a water line can be classified as ductile iron, cast iron, polymer (PVC), or concrete.

Intangible assets—refer to assets that have no boundaries and cannot generally be identified using the five senses. The most popular and relevant to industry are software programs and electronic data. As in the case of the other two asset types, subcategories can be assigned. Software subcategories include operating systems, productivity tools (e.g. MS Office), business applications (Administrative (HR/Payroll), Financial, Materials and Work Management, Production Scheduling)

Successful companies have made the link between maximizing asset performance and reliability and minimizing the costs of asset used to produce goods and services. They understand the relationship among the three key components in business operations (assets, people and processes) and have been able to skillfully balance the three components to sustain competitiveness. Asset Management can be loosely described as the practice of cost-effective exploitation of any asset over its lifecycle to strategically meet performance standards in a safe and environmentally sound manner. A more formal definition of asset management is given below.

Definition of Asset Management

Asset Management is the optimization of the lifecycle of an asset to meet performance standards in a safe and environmentally sound manner through smart Planning, Investment Financing, Engineering, Operations, Maintenance, Refurbishment and Replacement

DETAILED REVIEW OF THE ASSET LIFECYCLE

Figure 2.1 shows an asset lifecycle with nine distinct phases. All assets follow these lifecycle steps. Understanding the basic principles of each of these phases and the unique requirements of the asset type is critical to acquiring the right asset for your business. Each of these steps will be discussed in detail in the following paragraphs. The business practices for each phase will be discussed in Chapter 4.

Asset Life Cycle

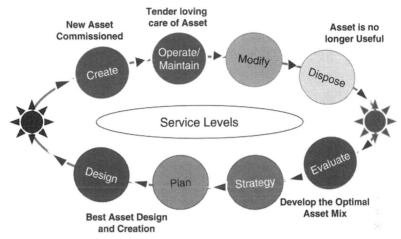

FIGURE 2.1 *The Eight Phases of the Asset Lifecycle.*

Stage 1: Evaluate and Identify a Need

Need identification is the most important stage of the asset lifecycle. Making the wrong decision at this stage can have major consequences over the rest of the life of the asset. Imagine the impact when we consider assets with lives 75–100 years! Identifying a need involves an analysis of changing client demands, a critical review of the ability of the current asset mix to meet these demands (through improved maintenance, upgrade or modification) and the impact of technological obsolescence. Demand and supply modeling is a key step in the process to ensure that resources are used wisely.

Building new assets when existing capacity is not utilized is a waste of critical resources. Supply-side review and modeling can ensure that existing assets are fully utilized. One example from the field involved an instrumentation technician at one manufacturing plant who was not able to maintain the instrument air flow and pressure needed to keep the automated system running properly. She made a request to purchase another air compressor. The experienced maintenance manager felt that the existing five compressor units should be adequate based on a quick comparison of rated versus demand capacities. He suggested they first embark on a leak detection program using ultrasonic tools. Both managers and technicians were surprised at the number of leaks they found that had been inaudible due to equipment noise. When the piping system was repaired and upgraded they were able to use three units to sustain process operations and keep two on standby, instead of having to purchase a sixth unit! A current trend is to acquire similar companies and take many similar processes or manufacturing facilities out of service when inefficient operations are optimized.

Demand-side modeling can be based on projected consumer needs as a result of increased market share from an aggressive sales campaign or growth in the market. In the water and energy markets, aggressive conservation programs have been able to reduce the demand for these products and free up capacity for legitimate demand increases. Another example is the sound advice from environmentalist to walk, use a bicycle, take the train or bus to work and leave your vehicle at home, in order to reduce the number of cars on the road and use up available capacity of other assets to reduce air pollution.

There are many technology tools for demand- and supply-side modeling. Most of these tools are unique to the industry (e.g., hydraulic models for water and waste water operations). It is important you identify the right tool for your industry and practice effective demand and supply-side analysis before you invest scarce resources into new assets. Once the need for a new asset is determined, formal planning is necessary.

Stage 2: Develop an Asset Strategy

When the decision is made to create a new asset, you need a high-level asset strategy before any further planning or detailed work can be done. Strategy sets the stage for planning and design. The key things to consider here are:

(1) Estimated economic asset life and overall project life—the business case has to consider regular replacements in order to keep the business in existence. In this case, O&M staff can provide valuable information on average refurbishment intervals and approximate costs. In addition, they can provide the accurate ongoing routine maintenance costs necessary to keep the asset in good shape.

(2) Funding strategy (how much capital should be raised and how can it be raised to fund the creation, operation and maintenance of the asset)—existing cash, bonds etc. This is linked with item 3 below, type of ownership.

(3) Type of ownership—this can be fully owned and operated by you, leased, rented, franchise, Design Build Operate (DBO), or a Public

Private Partnership (P3). Recently, there's been a trend in the private sector and even in the public sector to the latter three types, because clients would like to avoid the headaches and challenges associated with managing people and using them to operate and maintain assets. The suggested ownership models hold new challenges in the management of the partnership. Managers need to ensure that the investment shareholders or citizens have made in the assets is managed responsibly and there is an effective quality- assurance and control process in place. Choices in these areas will determine how planning and design will be done.

Stage 3: Planning

The level of planning is dictated by the criticality and investment costs associated with the asset. At this stage it is advisable to conduct a proper economic analysis presenting a winning proposal for investment funds. The net present value (NPV) concept is the preferred economic tool. In the event that the proposal is for replacement of an existing asset (at the end of its life), proper documentation is necessary to support the recommendation to replace the asset. O&M staff must work closely with engineering and finance personnel to prepare a proposal that will have a great chance of competing for scarce funds. In many cases a project with great NPV is just the start to the planning process. Securing the funding from bondholders or raising rates to finance the project may be the biggest challenge at this stage. Each category of asset or major asset should have an asset plan.

Stage 4: Design

Approval to proceed with a project for a new asset sets the stage for the design process. The rule of thumb at this juncture it is to involve the O&M staff, if you want to create an asset that will serve the needs of the end-user. Many effective design engineers credit their success to the practical ideas and suggestions they get from O&M staff. Designers are aware that their relatively brief involvement (3–6 months) is the basis for operating and maintaining an asset for the rest of its life. When engineers do not communicate with O&M staff, they can create assets that are difficult to maintain and are incompatible with existing infrastructure (with consequent training, spares, and operating procedure issues). In addition, it is not uncommon to find assets installed with limited access and lifting facilities for maintenance at some sites. Designers must design for reliability and maintainability, and incorporate the latest technological advances with due consideration for safety and environmental needs. They should seek compatibility with the existing asset base. For simple assets, e.g., components of an existing process, design may be simply searching out the right unit in the market place, based on a facility's performance specifications. Major and complex facilities and processes will require specialized design expertise, in-house, external, or a combination of both. Pursuing options other than outright ownership of the asset will reduce the level of effort your staff needs to make at this stage.

Stage 5: Create—Procure/Build/Commission

Good project management with a focus on time, scope, money, and facility impact is important in the successful creation of an asset. It is important to follow your company's purchasing terms and guidelines in the sourcing, selection and procurement of any assets, components or materials that will be used for the project. The purchasing department is worth its weight in gold at this stage for ensuring that you obtain your assets or the components to create the assets at the correct specifications, right quality, on the promised date and with the necessary after-sales support. Involvement of O&M staff at key aspects of the project allows for a critical knowledge-transfer needed to operate and maintain the asset and also provides important quality control during the actual construction. At this stage also, all the necessary documentation needed to support operations and maintenance should be provided electronically to populate the Computerized Work Management System (CWMS), Geographical Information System (GIS), Supervisory Control and Data Acquisition (SCADA), Electronic Document Management System, Financial Information System (FIS), and Asset Management Systems.

The commissioning process in the past has served as the formal hand over of the asset (or project) to the owners. O&M personnel have always interpreted it as the event that starts a period of headache for them as they allow Engineering to get a signature and "wash their hands" from the project. They try to integrate the asset into the overall operations usually with limited resources, inadequate knowledge transfer, spare parts and documentation on the asset. In addition, both project managers, engineers, vendors and contractors have a vested interest in claiming success so that they can close out the project (a much anticipated milestone for the project manager) and secure final payments (critical to the vendor or contractor). The commissioning stage should be taken more seriously and should be viewed as an opportunity to provide all the baseline asset information that the O&M group will need to be able to be effective at maintaining the asset integrity and reliability needs to have with the asset in its original condition. It is also a great opportunity for Engineering to confirm their ongoing support for O&M and to seek feedback that could enhance their future designs and implementation processes project design and creation business processes.

Stage 6: *Operate* and Maintain

Operation is normally the longest stage of the asset lifecycle varying in time from one year for low-cost disposable assets to over 50 years. The operator is the single resource most associated with the asset over its lifetime. When properly trained on the operating procedures, an operator can use the asset in a safe manner to create the product or deliver the service that is required. Poor training or not understanding how the asset works can lead to asset failure, defective product, excess waste, asset damage, injuries, and high operating costs. In addition, there is always the potential for environmental problems, when assets are not operated properly. A good operator becomes attuned to the health of the asset and can be the first line of defense for asset care. Good operators use their five senses to continuously gather vital data and form a intuitive feel for the asset condition. Operators can call up maintenance to say that the machine has a "funny" noise or "something just doesn't feel right". Usually further inspection and troubleshooting by maintenance reveals the start of a problem that could have been catastrophic if it had not been caught. Many companies are taking operations to another level in asset care. Most companies are training up operators to perform autonomous maintenance. This concept requires that operators be given additional skills to perform "CLAIR"-type work, an acronym for the following five tasks:

- *C*—Cleaning, when assets are properly cleaned, there is a reduced possibility of foreign material getting into moving parts and causing deterioration or jams and eventual failures. Cleaning assets reveals cracks, loose parts and leaks that could contribute to larger failures. In addition, clean assets and a clean work area contribute to a safe working environment and a sense of pride in the job.
- *L*—Lubricate, lubrication is the lifeline for assets with moving parts. Inadequate lubrication or the wrong lubricant can result in accelerated wear and eventual asset failure, the inability of the asset to perform what is required by the user. A properly trained

operator can ensure that lubrication schedules, for any asset under her care, are done properly and on time. Many manufacturers are automating the lubrication process using lubricant cartridges, automated lubricating systems with grease or oil from a central reservoir piped to individual bearings. The operator can still play a role here in being vigilant and refilling the reservoirs with the proper lubricant on time and ensuring the system is working and lubricating is actually getting to the bearing or moving part. Good lubrication is a key factor in maximizing asset reliability.

- *A*—Adjust, many assets (e.g., automation end devices, instrumentation) go out of calibration over time and must be properly adjusted or calibrated to ensure that the product stays within the desired quality, as well as to ensure that the device will perform as required and protect the asset when there is an unexpected deviation from the set point.
- *I*—Inspection is usually done through the "operator rounds" aspect of operations. Unfortunately, many operators use this time only to ensure that the process is working as required and don't make the effort to get a feel for the health of the asset. Experienced operators use their senses to identify when the asset is operating outside the normal operating conditions. Good interpretation of the data can lead to a minor repair at low cost and minimum downtime compared to a major repair (high cost and downtime), if the early signs of deterioration are acted on quickly.
- *R*—Repair, operators can minimize downtime due to minor repairs if they are trained up to do these repairs competently and safely. This type of repair is usually restricted to small tasks using simple tools and done within a half an hour. The operator can easily tighten a loose fitting, guard, or change a belt and get the asset up and running long before maintenance employees respond. It is important the work and cost history are both recorded (usually using a CWMS) for future evaluation and decision making.

Maintain

Operations and maintenance are joined at the hip and must work together to maximize the return on investment in the asset. It is essential that maintenance tactics are developed to achieve cost-effective performance and optimal reliability of the asset. The appropriate mix of best-practices concepts such as Program Driven Work, Reliability Centered Maintenance, Predictive/Condition-Based Maintenance and Total Productive Maintenance should be used to support the work management process. This can result in what is termed Optimized Work—the right balance of Reactive and Proactive work on the asset. Data such as cost, work history and asset condition must be recorded on a regular basis during the course of doing work, so that asset deterioration curves can be plotted and economic analyses carried out to determine if the asset is doing its job in a cost-effective manner. These analyses determine if the asset should be modified or decommissioned and/or replaced and will be instrumental in driving the capital improvement program of the company. A popular trend is to have maintenance staff trained in basic operations skills, so that they can complete lower-level operations work without having the operator on site (this can be asset lock and tag outisolation or commissioning after repairs).

Stage 7: Modify

Ongoing monitoring of asset performance and projected changes in demand may dictate the need to modify the asset. In addition, there may be safety or environmental drivers requiring asset upgrade. Any projects needing modification should also be supported by a proper economic evaluation. Any modifications should follow sound engineering design standards and should, at a minimum, have input from operations, maintenance, and engineering. The asset database should be updated to reflect all changes to the asset (technical specifications, operating and maintenance manuals as well as financial information) and be made available to relevant personnel.

Stage 8: Decommission (Dispose/Replace)

Disposal or replacement brings an end to the asset life cycle and in most cases is closely tied with the creation of a new asset as the old one is decommissioned, "moth-balled" or removed from site. Decommissioning may become necessary for a number of reasons—poor asset condition and uneconomic to refurbish. Decommissioning can be related to reduced demand for service or product, technological obsolescence and reduced demand for service or product. In the first two scenarios the asset must be removed from service, dismantled and sold for scrap ensuring that safety and environmental considerations should be incorporated into the salvage process. In the last scenario, then the key focus is to ensure that the asset is left in a state that ensures it is protected from degradation; cannibalization for spares and is properly secured. To ensure that it can be easily re-commissioned in the event that it becomes economically attractive to increase supply for the product or service. In the event that the asset must be salvaged, then safety and environmental considerations should be incorporated into the salvage process. As in the modification stage, the asset database should be updated to reflect the changes in asset status.

PLAYERS INVOLVED IN THE ASSET LIFECYCLE

Many resources are involved in the different lifecycle phases of an asset. Unfortunately, most of these players concentrate on doing a good job in their area of responsibility without involving the others. The result is usually a less that optimal choice of asset and mediocre performance when it is commissioned. In most companies, we have found, the typical frontline roles involved in the management of the asset lifecycle are:

- Engineer:
  —Modeling Engineer
  —Design Engineer
  —Construction/Project Manager
- Operator:
  —Various classifications (Operator 1, 2, 3, 4) based on the type of process
- Maintainer:
  —Mechanic
  —Electrician
  —Instrumentation Technician
  —Planner
  —Scheduler
- Stores person
- Buyer
- Safety Officer
- Quality Controller
- Accountant
- Information Technology Support—e.g. System Administrator for the CWMS
- Human resources internal consultant

The above list is not all-inclusive and can vary depending on the type of process and asset. What is obvious is that there are many different roles (usually filled by one person). As the number of roles increases, it becomes more difficult to achieve the right level of coordination over the lifecycle. In an effort to address this challenge, many companies are grouping roles into one job description (where it makes sense) to improve task coordination and ultimately asset performance and reliability. Many companies are moving to job titles such as Plant Technicians (in contrast to "operators"), who do CLAIR work in addition to operations), Electrical and Instrumentation Control Technician, and Planner/Scheduler.

ASSET MANAGEMENT AND THE OTHER KEY BUSINESS PROCESSES

Nine major business processes in the typical industry are focused on the asset lifecycle. These are:

(1) Asset Management
(2) Financial Management
(3) Capital Projects (design and construction) for new or upgrade of existing assets
(4) Purchasing Management
(5) Inventory Management
(6) Work Management or Maintenance Management
(7) Operations Management
(8) Customer Service
(9) Safety and Environmental Management

Asset management provides the framework for the above processes to work effectively in delivering a product or service to a customer. In Chapter 5, each of these processes will be discussed with respect to their relevance to asset management.

CHAPTER 3

Drivers for Asset Management

DRIVERS FOR ASSET MANAGEMENT

Current Asset Management Practices

Asset management is poorly understood and poorly practiced in most industries today. Many view asset management as what the finance staff does from a tracking and reporting standpoint. Some see asset management as a computerized work management system or condition auditing of assets. Teams that create new assets are just focused on getting the asset in place within the scope and budget. Operations and maintenance personnel are usually caught up in a reactive mode of working and focus on keeping the assets functional.

Industries are infrastructure-intensive, and the average asset life can vary from 10 years in the manufacturing sector to over 50 years in the public sector. Many assets are way past their economic life or have been completely rebuilt or overhauled during their lifespan. Effective asset management should ensure that this infrastructure can meet performance needs in a safe and environmentally sound manner at minimum cost. In addition, there is a responsibility in many industries for the asset to look aesthetically pleasing. Many industries fall short in these areas. In the US alone it is estimated that there is a $70 Billion[1] infrastructure deficit. In the petroleum industries, past variations in oil prices have limited funding for upkeep of assets, and many facilities are being operated in a man-

---

[1]EPA Documentation on W/WW Infrastructure

ner to squeeze out additional production with minimal asset maintenance. The 2003 electricity blackout in eastern US and Canada was attributed to poor asset management of the transmission and distribution system. In evaluating if your company practices asset management and how well it is being done, there are fundamental questions to be addressed:

(1) What assets do you own?
(2) Which are the critical ones?
(3) What is the lifecycle cost data associated with each asset
(4) What is the current condition?
(5) What is the deterioration rate?
(6) What are the market, book and replacement values of the asset?
(7) How is your firm organized to take care of assets?
  (a) Do you have the right skills and team arrangements?
  (b) Are you proactively developing the new skills needed to meet the changing demands of the business environment?
  (c) What are your recruitment, retention and succession planning strategies?
(8) What business processes are needed to maximize reliability and performance and reduce costs?
(9) Are you leveraging the appropriate technology assets in support of asset management—hardware, business software, automation and control?
(10) How do you manage the integrated technology asset solution?
(11) How do you manage all knowledge around the assets. How do you capture, store, continuously update, and share this knowledge?
(12) Do you have a 20-year capital program that provides short, medium and long-term plans for asset modifications, upgrade, or replacements?
(13) Is the Capital program for asset-related projects driven by economic parameters such as Net Present Value (NPV), Rate of Return on Investment (ROI) and Payback Period
(14) Do you have standards for asset-related processes around each phase of the asset lifecycle?

Many executives would be shocked by the answers to the above questions. On the other hand, replies to the questions can provide an indication of the asset management opportunities that exist in your operation. (A detailed asset management review is given in Chapter 10.)

WHY ASSET MANAGEMENT NOW—IS THE URGENCY REAL?

Ineffective asset management is a direct contributor to the lack of competitiveness and sustainability of your company. Poor asset management leads to:

(1) High initial asset costs (increasing capacity when it is not required or ineffective use of existing facilities, high project costs because of poor project management practices).

(2) Reactive work environments and high O&M costs associated with the assets.

(3) Ineffective work coordination around the asset lifecycle and resulting low labor productivity.

(4) Large asset infrastructure condition deficit.

(5) Increase in safety issues.

(6) Difficulty meeting both safety and environmental regulations.

(7) Difficulty capturing, updating and sharing asset-related knowledge critical to competitiveness and sustainability.

(8) Overall higher costs to create your product or service.

(9) Inability to sustain a competitive edge in the marketplace.

(10) Problems in increasing value for shareholders.

(11) Reduced market share.

(12) Missed opportunities because of capacity or performance issues.

(13) Worst case—bankruptcy.

DRIVERS FOR STRATEGIC ASSET MANAGEMENT

For a company to change there must be a clear vision of what the company is to look like. Drivers are what influences this vision. Drivers that are identified and dealt with on a proactive basis can be the difference between success and failure or excellent and sub-optimal performance. The following business drivers are directly related to asset management or in some way influence how a company manages and operates its assets.

Higher Customer Expectations

Customers are very demanding of value for money in today's marketplace. Poor product quality, high prices, or indifferent service can easily cause customers to shift to a competitors product or service. In the private sector this can mean outsourcing of operations to countries with lower production costs. In the public arena this may lead to privatization, where private operators compete to provide a service or at a lower cost than governmental agencies.

Large Infrastructure Condition Gap

Many industries, and especially those in the public sector, are facing a significant gap in infrastructure condition. Sewers, water lines, electricity transmission and distribution grids are very old and in many instances are well beyond their economic lives. The funding required to bring these assets to the desired condition or to replace them with modern and efficient assets is very difficult to come by without raising rates or taxes. Persons responsible for taking care of these assets can adopt the out of sight, out of mind approach and react only when an emergency occurs, such as a collapsed sewer, broken water line, or electrical grid failure. More alarming is when companies introduce new assets into their operations (new developments, new factories etc.) and continue to apply the same old business practices, people and asset strategies. The result is that the new assets quickly end up in the same state as the old ones!

Need to be Competitive—Lower O&M Costs

Pressures from low-cost or more competitive producers or service providers have forced many companies to go for the quick-fix. There is an unrelenting push to cut costs. Often senior management reduces the O&M and the Capital Improvement Program budgets without grasping the effects on asset management. The effects are not seen immediately. Often they surface in the form of major or catastrophic failures. O&M is forced to reduce staff, materials costs, or to use old and unreliable tools and equipment, while support groups (e.g., Information Technology) keep increasing their budgets to hire new staff.

Competition for Funds

Globalization and the internet enable customers to have many different (and cheaper) options for satisfying their needs. To be competitive companies must keep costs down and invest in new technologies to improve throughput and product quality. Stiff competition for limited funds requires that budget proposals be based on solid data and demonstrate the return on investment to the company. O&M has traditionally struggled in this area because of poor data and an inability to develop convincing business cases for new assets, upgrades or modifications. They thus suffer the consequences of reduced budgets. Reduced O&M funding leads directly to poor asset management and diminished competitiveness.

Need to Meet Regulations(USA[2]—GASB 34, CMOM, Canada[3] Bills 175, 195)

Concern about public health and well being is driving many regulations, which in turn are forcing service providers to demonstrate better stewardship and accountabilities for their assets. Sadly, as in the case of the Walkerton Water Crisis in Ontario, Canada, where seven people died and thousands fell ill due to poor water quality, it took loss of lives and pain and suffering for people to understand the importance of proper asset management. Many communities are being asked to implement full cost-recovery models supported by leading business practices, asset strategies, and people-related concepts to ensure that assets perform to the desired standards of high reliability and minimum costs. In the private sector, companies are being pressured to ensure that workplace standards are in place in third-world countries, where they have moved production offshore in search of the competitive edge. Eventually, wages in these countries will catch up with the first-world countries, and then the competitive edge will have to be achieved the hard way—through the introduction and practice of good asset management strategies.

Privatization Threats

In many instances, municipalities are turning to private operators for service delivery in the hope that costs and service levels are more in line with their customers expectations. In the public arena when service is poor, it can mean citizen rebellion—with holders of public office being voted out. With this threat hanging over them, elected officials turn to other options for service providers (e.g., privatization of the entire operation, P3s (public private partnerships), and DBOs—design, build, operate arrangements).

Baby Boomer Effect (Looming Major Retirement Crisis) and Potential Loss of Asset Related Corporate Knowledge

So-called baby boomers (people born during the period 1945 to 1960)

[2]US GASB 34, CMOM
[3]Canada MOE (Ontario)

will be retiring in droves over the next five to ten years. The knowledge to care for assets often resides only in the brains of individuals from this generation or in paper documents. The potential loss of this knowledge and their company's competitive edge is a concern on the minds of CEOs today. This concern is driving many companies to develop knowledge management practices with supporting technologies to ensure that the know-how to operate and maintain their assets remains in the company as people retire.

Growth in Population, Market Share Etc.

Not all assets are falling apart. Many private companies are enjoying success with high growth and increasing market share. They are flush with cash and can underwrite large investments in new assets as well as upgrade, modify, and replace underperforming assets. Similarly, many cities and municipalities are experiencing high population growths and are investing in new infrastructure (roads, sewers, water and waste water plants, parks and recreational areas and new office buildings). Many of these companies will enjoy a honeymoon period where assets will continue to meet performance standards, while the assets slowly deteriorate. If companies do not practice effective asset management strategies, they will end up in the same situation that many companies face today.

More Advanced Technology/Designs Available—Obsolete Assets

The engineering community has devised new ways to build products to meet the needs of society. Advances in information technology, light weight, durable materials, and more efficient processes have resulted in more technologically advanced assets being available. The latter can now produce products more reliably and at lower costs than existing assets. Many companies now have to consider the difficult decision of whether to upgrade or replace existing asset infrastructure to stay competitive.

Asset Management and the Triple Bottom Line

Some of the excellent companies that operate in the world today have been around for many years (in some case over 100 years). They have recognized that focusing on profitability alone does not provide sustainability for the company. These companies have been focusing on the triple bottom line. They seek to balance the economic, environmental and societal aspects of business in evaluating success. Asset management spans all three areas and is a key enabler of triple bottom line goals and objectives.

It is clear there are many important drivers in the business environment for strategic asset management. Companies who embrace asset management strategies and proactively invest to ensure managing assets is a core behavior will reap the elusive benefits of sustainability, high customer satisfaction, high profitability, a positive environmental and safety record, reputation as a good corporate citizen, and happy and satisfied employees. The following chapters discuss the various asset management strategies and how they can be implemented successfully.

CHAPTER 4

Making the Case for Asset Management

With any major initiative or change process, a compelling business case is essential. Many company leaders have failed to gain support for their asset management initiative because they have not been able to convince key decision makers and stakeholders that the program is a good investment. Most senior managers still operate on the premise that if I give you one dollar and you can give me many more back, then this must be a good investment of company funds and resources. This notion is important in deciding where limited funds go. In an environment where people responsible for taking care of assets cannot effectively develop and sell a sound business case for an asset management program, company performance will eventually suffer.

IDENTIFYING THE NEED FOR AN ASSET MANAGEMENT PROGRAM

Decision makers look for tangible returns on any investment, in line with the generally accepted economic criteria of Net present Value (or Net Present Worth), Return on Investment (ROI), and Payback Period. These indicators can be developed for any project using the business case concept, where dollar inflows (benefits) and outflows (costs) are modeled on a spreadsheet over the life of the project. The economic indicators are the key output from the business case. A practical asset management program must start with the signs of ineffective or non-existent asset management practices.

Within a business signs pointing to the need for asset management can be identified at each phase of the asset lifecycle. The following are some indicators to look for:

Stage 1——Evaluate and Identify a Need

Poor supply/demand analysis—there is existing unused asset capacity, but new assets are being created anyway. This can be because of inadequate O&M practices that have assets working at low efficiencies. Analyzing the root causes of the problems and devising improvement plans can reduce these types of efficiencies to desired levels.

All players not involved in this stage—another issue here is that both activities can be occurring independently—with new assets being created without a full understanding of the capability of existing assets.

Stage 2 and Stage 3—Develop an Asset Strategy/Plan

Overall strategy over the asset lifecycle for the asset not developed—there is no clear strategy for management of the asset when it is in place.

Resource plan for operating and maintaining the asset is not clear—O&M are left to figure out reactively what are the skills, job descriptions, and staffing numbers necessary to manage the asset and achieve its true performance potential.

No business case for the asset has been developed—poor analysis of costs and benefits results in the project being a non-starter or severely under-budgeted. In the latter instance, to complete the project without cost overruns, engineers resort to cutting corners to the detriment of the overall cost of ownership. Such behavior also reduces O&M's ability to manage the asset.

Stage 4—Design

None or very little end-user involvement—there are many examples of the effect of a siloed view on asset design, where all of the right players are not involved. Traditionally, O&M have not been brought into the design process. In fact, other groups, such as Materials Management, Health and Safety, in-house security experts, and Human Resources can furnish valuable input for the design process.

Cheap designs to stay within budget—in truth you get what you pay for the asset. Low-cost designs will enable you to have a project completed on a small budget, but the follow-on costs to operate and maintain the asset may be enormous. Of course, budgets limit what can be realistically done. However, good research plus involvement of the materials management group and O&M can lead to cost-effective solutions.

Engineers and designers are unaware of technology advances or ignore them because they are too expensive or untested—once the decision to move forward with construction has been made, it is very costly to make changes in design. Without adequate research it is possible to overlook or miss advanced technology opportunities that create valuable savings in O&M costs and also help meet environmental regulations.

Stage 5—Create—Procure/Build/Commission

Project management issues around time scope and money—poor project management practices can lead to high cost overruns and can sometimes result in cutting corners. In addition, there may be reluctance on the part of the project manager to seek a change order for incorporating modifications or new technologies that can make a vast difference to subsequent O&M costs.

Very conservative approaches to purchasing—cheapest is best—this is one of the biggest complaints by engineering and O&M. Strong asset management standards, clear specifications, and good communications can help resolve this issue.

Little consideration for O&M—"complete project and get out" becomes a watchword. O&M is left with assets that are not interchangeable, or are missing documentation and insurance spares. Improvisation and "go figure out" become the main agenda.

Stage 6—*Operate* and Maintain

High asset downtime—these are usually easy records to discover, since equipment downtime is directly related to production or service and is usually tracked closely by senior management. Equipment downtime can be due to operational or process problems and changeovers. An evaluation of process upsets of asset downtime/failure due to operator error will indicate the level of impact that operators are having on the performance and health of the asset.

Relationship with Operations—high conflict with maintenance staff and regular playing of the "blame game" are further signs there is an urgent need to develop a common sense of purpose for asset management.

Maintain

Asset Registry—incomplete or non-existent registry, poor asset data, and very little effort to classify assets in a meaningful way are indicative of opportunities in the asset management area.

High asset downtime—the other aspect of downtime (the first was discussed under the "Operate" phase) is that which is due to maintenance repairs (proactive or reactive). This information is very useful in justifying an asset management program. Sometimes this data is viewed differently as equipment uptime, i.e., the percentage of time that the equipment is available for use. This should be in the range of (95–100%) % depending on the industry. High percentage of reactive work results in a high maintenance cost. Reactive work encompasses breakdown maintenance, corrective maintenance (that can be planned) due to secondary damage from breakdowns as well as any other unplanned work. Reactive work is also characterized by very little planning and scheduling, poor support from inventory and purchasing, a very high work-order backlog and a high cost of maintenance (labor, services and materials). There is a high degree of non-value-added work, such as waiting for materials, tools, or equipment to be available for work to be done, excessive traveling, wrong parts, inaccurate assessment of the work to be done etc. The ideal balance of reactive to proactive work should be 25% to 75% respectively.

Poor Preventive Maintenance (PM) Program—a poor PM program is a good indicator that an asset management program can be beneficial to your organization. Inadequate numbers of PMs and/or poor quality PMs, together with very low PM compliance, are sure signs that the workforce is struggling to maintain assets.

Poor asset reliability (Mean Time Between Failures)—Low asset reliability, signaled by very frequent failures (small interval between failures), is another indication that the workforce is not in control of the maintenance operations. There are usually numerous repetitive high-cost failures, which are easily overlooked in the daily panic and fire-fighting mode of operating.

Relationship with Operations—frequent conflict with operations staff is a sign there is an urgent need to take control of the work and maximize performance of the assets. There is general feeling of frustration and inability to change things.

Poor Inventory and Purchasing Control and Management—Absence of inventory control is characterized by poor stores service level (<95%), high numbers of stock items and also high numbers of stock outs, long lead times for replenishment of the inventory, low inventory turnover ratios (<2.0), and high inventory value. This is extremely important when it relates to MRO (Maintenance, Repair and Overhaul) spares. A large number of obsolete spares being maintained in stock is an indication of poor lifecycle planning. Poor purchasing support is also characterized by a lack of confidence in the buyers, due to long waits for non stores and services purchase orders, poor quality items, or unwillingness by the purchasing group to listen to the needs of operations and maintenance.

Few or no records—the inability to find asset work and cost records, documentation on PMs and work order closeout information is an indication of an ad hoc or chaotic approach to asset management.

Safety and the environment—a high number of safety issues or violations of regulatory standards (both safety and environmental) is typical of a reactive way of working and indicative of poor asset management practices in the "maintain" stage of the asset lifecycle. Good asset management practices can provide the means to take control of the operations and reduce or eliminate hazards.

High overtime and staffing levels—the typical reaction to dealing with an out-of-control work situation is to throw money and people at it. This can mean high overtime to complete work and get equipment back into production, premium prices for much needed spares or services, or replacing complete components or pieces of equipment. In addition, there is a tendency to overstaff maintenance and operations groups at all levels to manage out-of-control situations.

Stage 7—Modify/Upgrade

Ineffective capital improvement program (CIP) for existing assets—the CIP is focused mainly on new assets and is based on an inadequate or superficial demand/supply side analysis. Projects for upgrade or modifications to existing assets are not well defined or planned and are funded only in cases of extremely high priority, such as unsafe situations resulting from the asset. There is no real economic justification for projects, subjective rationale is provided together with a lot of begging for a share in the CIP funds.

Lack of continuous improvement (CI) program—there is no formal continuous improvement. Employees may come up with ideas, but these are not generally supported by solid data and usually don't make it through to implementation. Asset failures are not generally investigated and repairs are rushed (at high cost) to get the asset back into production. An environment of "do what you are told and don't ask questions" usually prevails.

Very little use of data for decision making—this environment is characterized by very little technology for capturing asset related data or stand-alone simple systems. Use of the systems is limited and many users do not see the value of using technology solutions. Data quality and integrity are poor. Employees prefer to use gut feelings or experience to drive decision making.

No current or recent asset condition audit—asset condition data is very limited and usually outdated. Key parameters required to know the condition of the asset on its deterioration curve are poorly defined or do not exist. If asked to give an indication of the health of an asset, the response by owners or caretakers is based on their recent memories of failures or how the asset looks and sounds currently when it is working. For assets that are not visible, e.g. underground infrastructure, assessing the condition of the asset is guesswork.

Stage 8—Decommission (Dispose/Replace)

Ineffective capital program (program not supported by proper supply and demand modeling)—the same discussion as in Stage 7 (Modify or Upgrade) also applies in this phase. In many situations an inadequate demand and supply side evaluation may result in assets that are not needed. If current assets are poorly maintained, it is possible that these assets are performing below capacity. A closer look at the causes of poor performance and resolution of the root causes (not the symptoms) will yield dramatic improvements in asset effectiveness (efficiency and cost performance). Possibly there is no need for further assets. The case study on air compressors discussed in Chapter 2 illustrates this point well. In the public service sector, e.g. water, wastewater, electricity and solid waste industries, good conservation programs can minimize the amount of new infrastructure added each year despite continued growth.

High level of obsolete assets (cheaper, more efficient and technology advanced assets available)—poor asset management over time can lead to an infrastructure mix totally out of step with modern designs and technological advances. In this case the company is probably close to going out of business, unless it is a monopoly with a captive market. Today, advanced machine design, light and durable materials, automation, and control can lead to smaller, safer, more energy efficient, higher output, and more reliable assets. These assets can be very cost effective and for many North American companies advanced technology is the only way they can stave off global pressures from countries with lower production costs due to low wage rates.

Lots of complaints from O&M about old, decrepit, inefficient, unsafe and difficult to maintain assets—In a business environment characterized by complaints, there is a sense of hopelessness and despair. A vicious cycle ensues. Reduced profitability causes management to react to shareholder demands for returns on their investments and they seek

Asset Management Assessment

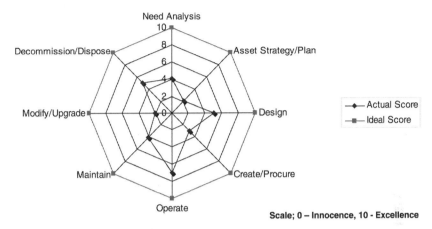

FIGURE 4.1 *Lifecycle-Based Asset Management Assessment.*

short-term solutions—often by reducing the capital improvement program (CIP) and maintenance budgets. The result is further deterioration in asset performance and reliability and continued reduction in profitability, culminating in most cases with the company going out of business or being bought by a competitor.

The above indicators can be represented in a radar diagram. An example of an assessment that shows that there is compelling need for asset management is given in Figure 4.1.

The areas discussed above are good high-level indicators of a business environment that is ripe with opportunities in the asset management area. This kind of review can be easily done using your own resources to get a high level indication of where your organization is on the asset management index. Scores can be averaged to develop an Asset Management index (AMI) and can be interpreted using the following simple guide, Table 4.1.

THE ASSET MANAGEMENT EVALUATION
AND BUSINESS CASE DEVELOPMENT

Once the overall need for an asset management program has been established, a detailed evaluation must be conducted. A sample evaluation

TABLE 4.1.   The Asset Management Index (AMI).

Asset Management Index (AMI)	Interpretation	Opportunity
0–2	Innocence	You cannot claim ignorance any-more—inaction will see your company go the route of the dinosaurs!
3–4	Awareness	Seek to better understand what asset management can do for your com-pany; develop and implement a suit-able program—get help!
5–6	Understanding	Need to get going and implement the various asset lifecycle strategies.
7–8	Competence	A focus on continuous improvement will yield further asset management opportunities.
9–10	Excellence	Implement knowledge development, management and retention strategies to sustain high-caliber performance.

is provided in Appendix 4.1. It is important that the components of an as-set management program are clearly defined, so costs can be identified for a cost-benefit analysis. A small team of up to six people should be created and be given the mandate and all the necessary support by senior management to conduct the detailed evaluations and subsequent busi-ness case for asset management. Recommendations for team members would be knowledgeable representatives from departments that focus on the various areas of the asset lifecycle. There should be at least one mem-ber from Planning, Engineering, Finance, Materials Management (Pur-chasing/Inventory), Operations, Maintenance and Information Technology. Select a team leader who has an overall grasp of the com-pany's operations—plus sufficient authority to demonstrate the importance management has given to the project.

CONDUCTING THE AM CURRENT-STATE ANALYSIS

The following steps are recommended for conducting the review to identify, quantify and validate the data needed to develop the business case for asset management:

Develop a team charter—a team charter is a critical tool to ensure that the AM team clearly understands their mandate, extent of authority, milestones, deliverables and relationships with other teams or groups (an example of a team charter is given in Appendix 4.2).

Orientation on asset management—provide education to team members on basic asset management concepts. This can be achieved by attending conferences, inviting experts to present on the subject, reading articles or books on the subject. What's learned can be distilled into a simple presentation the team can use for knowledge transfer to stakeholders.

Develop a vision, mission statements and an implementation roadmap—change requires a clear vision of what lies ahead and what the various steps are involved in getting there. Many affected personnel want to know what's in it for them, what new behaviors they need to embrace, and what change means for the company and customers (or society) overall. Vision and mission statements on asset management together with an easy-to-read roadmap to achieve the vision are key requirements for initiating the change needed to design and implement a sustainable asset management program.

Communication plan—the right message to stakeholders on a timely basis is important to buy-in for the project. It also ensures that staff does not misinterpret the team members' review as another management exercise aimed at another round of cost cutting and lay-offs. A sample communication plan is provided in Appendix 4.3.

Identify sources of information—this step in the process allows the team to evaluate where they can obtain information to conduct the review. Information is obtained from: paper records (project files, asset condition audits, capital improvement program), electronic records, site visits to plant and machinery, and interviews. It is desirable to follow the order given, with the interviews being the last step in the information-seeking process. The first three should provide good insight into what is going on and can be validated or adjusted based on interview responses. In each of the above categories, the team must be clear on what type of data is required. These sources of information will determine where to visit, interview questions, what paper reports to request and what reports to run. The questions and topics given in Appendix 4.1 are a good guide for this step.

Conduct desk audit—Review existing Asset Management Key Performance Indicators (KPI), existing benchmark information and the quality of existing data. It is important that the team documents key benchmarks for the critical information. Benchmarks are needed to analyze the gap in desired versus existing performance. Here the focus should be on efficiency *and* effectiveness indicators. A listing of the indicators is given in Chapter 13.

Review electronic data—It is important that the team understands the existing technology environment that supports asset management in the company. This should include details on all the existing business applications, databases, data records, networking and hardware infrastructure. System performance, limitations of existing applications and interfaces, quality of data etc. are very useful to the evaluation effort. The IT member of the team can obtain this information.

Conduct site visits—The asset management team must visit all facilities and conduct a visual inspection of each asset. This is by no means a comprehensive condition audit, but will certainly give a good feel for the current condition of the assets. The data, combined with asset history and cost data, will give a more accurate picture of asset condition. The comprehensive asset condition audit is usually done at the implementation stage of an asset management program.

Conduct interviews—Conduct confidential interviews with personnel (management, supervisory and frontline) in the various departments. Interviews should try to flesh out the concerns that people have in the business processes related to each phase pf the asset lifecycle, the relationships of individual units in the company, and the level of satisfaction with the support from these groups or departments.

Observe business practices related to assets—The team should be given the time to observe all the key business practices and identify the value-added and non-value-added steps in the process. The CIP planning, financing, project management processes, planning and scheduling of jobs, job execution, inventory and purchasing processes are key processes to be reviewed. This can be a good opportunity to have frank discussions with the people who are responsible for doing work. An effort should be made to allocate time frames to the activities being observed, without making people feel they are being measured.

Define the "as is" business processes—In order to fully understand what is happening in the various stages of the asset lifecycle, the team should first try to understand what personnel do in the various departments responsible for the lifecycle stages. To accomplish this, a detailed mapping of the existing business processes has to be conducted. Every effort should be made to identify the steps in each process and the different players who are involved in the steps. The data collected from the inquiries described above is very useful for this activity. It may be necessary to invite the people actually involved in the processes to participate in the mapping. This activity can be documented using flip charts and "post it" notes to define the process flow. It can also be done on a computer with a process-mapping tool such as MS Visio and a data projection system. The final result should be a detailed process map for each of the key business processes, together with notes on who is involved in each step, the estimated time and costs, and any other relevant information. It is important to note any "hand-off" from steps that lead to other processes. For example, in the planning process there will be a hand off to the engineering and finance departments to develop business cases and budgets for projects in the CIP before engineering can proceed to detailed design. Some asset management practitioners prefer to do a less detailed review at this stage, namely, one that's sufficient to win approval for the program. A more detailed review ("As Is" documentation) is done at the implementation instead of the planning stage.

IDENTIFY AND QUANTIFY THE BENEFITS AND SAVINGS

The benefits of a sustainable AM program can be divided into two categories: tangible and intangible. The following discussion explains anticipated savings and also provides an estimated range of savings based on the experience of the author as well as documentation by various other writers in the asset management field.

TANGIBLE BENEFITS OF SUSTAINABLE ASSET MANAGEMENT PROGRAM

Improved Effectiveness of the CIP

A capital program that guarantees new assets are added only if they are really needed and the right assets are modified, upgraded in a timely manner based on solid economic rationale can lead to a 5% reduction in CIP annual budget in the second year of implementation. This can be increased by a further 2% savings if best-in-class project management techniques are consistently applied with an unrelenting focus on time, scope, money and impact on the existing operations. The overall savings in the CIP area can be 7% of the annual budget.

Increased Asset Uptime and Effectiveness through an Optimized Maintenance Program

A move from reactive to proactive maintenance can lead to a 40% reduction in O&M costs. This can be achieved through equal reductions in O&M budgets over a four-year period (the time it takes to successfully implement best in class O&M strategies).

Reduced Material Management Costs

Reduced Material Costs

Fewer failures and better inventory management will yield savings of 10–30% of the annual material cost associated with doing work. This can be 10% in the first year of system implementation, 20% in the second year and 30% in the third year and 30% thereafter on an annual basis.

Reduced Stock

The actual number of stock items and the average quantities stocked can be reduced to optimal levels based on solid inventory management practices. Such practices entail only required addition of new stock items, removal of obsolete, slow-moving items, and optimal Reorder Points (ROPs), Reorder Quantities (ROQs) and Safety Stock levels. The associated inventory value reduction can range from 5%–15% of the existing value of the Inventory. In the first year of system implementation there can be a 5% saving, followed by a 10% saving in the second year and 15% thereafter on an annual basis.

Reduced Labor Costs

Automation and control can lead to a significant reduction in operations staff based on the extent of existing automation. Savings can range from 10 to 20% for a semi automated operations. (In the case of a highly manual operation, savings can range from 20 to 40% through reductions in the labor force.)

Planning and Scheduling

Good planning and scheduling of work using an integrated technology asset solution, together with the elimination of non-valued added time such as waiting, delays etc., can free up at least 5% of the maintenance work force in the second year of implementation. This can improve further to 10% per year by the end of the third year and 20% per year after.

Inventory and Purchasing Management

Best in class inventory and purchasing practices (with the elimination of the non-value added activities and use of JIT, consignment and preferred vendor arrangements) can translate into a staff reduction in both these areas of 10% in the second year and 20% per year after the third year of implementation.

Overtime

Overtime can be reduced by 5% in the first year, 10% in the second year and 15% per year after the third year of implementation. Overtime tends to be minimal after the third year of implementation of the program.

Absenteeism

Absenteeism can be reduced by 5% per year due to better control of the work, fewer emergency and poorly planned jobs, fewer safety issues and stressed employees.

Energy Costs

Increased asset reliability and efficiency can reduce the power required to start and operate motors or engines. Technologically advanced motors can reduce the energy necessary to move the same load. Increased equipment availability can provide the flexibility to operate additional equipment during off peak periods. Such strategies can translate into energy savings from 5% in the second year to 10% per year after the third year of implementing the program.

Continuous Improvement Projects

Good quality data captured by the enabling integrated asset technology solution can be a key source of information for initiating improvement projects in the operations. These can be related to workflow and can result in more cost-effective practices or can be related to asset replacement decision based on cost and work history captured on assets. Overall these projects can realize an average saving of 5% per year on operations and maintenance costs and can be realized from the third year after implementation.

INTANGIBLE BENEFITS OF A SUSTAINABLE ASSET MANAGEMENT PROGRAM

Moving from a reactive asset management culture to a sustainable and cost-effective program based on the asset lifecycle and a focus on minimal overall cost of ownership provides intangible benefits that can go a long way to selling an AM project to senior management. Intangible benefits include:

- Better staff motivation, commitment and coordination around the asset lifecycle.
- Better trained staff who are prepared to be empowered and take on new roles and responsibilities.
- A work culture that embraces change and smarter ways of working using technology (this makes it easier to make future changes).
- Reduced or zero safety and environmental issues.
- Proper documentation of work plans for assets, cost and work history for continuity when workers move on to other department or retire and for supporting ISO requirements (quality, safety, environmental).
- More reliable assets provide greater flexibility for the sales and production staff in meeting market demands and changes.
- Good quality information available to everyone for day to day decision making as well as to support continuous improvement initiatives.
- Good quality data on assets to support cost effective management of asset lifecycle.
- Corporate knowledge retention necessary to support a succession planning strategy and continuity of the business.

The above benefits are summarized in Table 4.2. (Benefits from implementing a Sustainable Asset management program):

COSTS ASSOCIATED WITH DEVELOPING AND IMPLEMENTING AN ASSET MANAGEMENT PROGRAM

Numerous costs are associated with the design and implementation of an asset management program. These can be direct investments at the beginning of the program, additional injection of funds at specific stages of the implementation, annual maintenance and system support costs as well as the use of internal resources. It is extremely important that all these costs are properly identified and estimated to develop a realistic business plan.

TABLE 4.2. *Tangible benefits from implementing an Asset Management program.*

Benefit	Cost saving (% of annual associated cost)									
	Yr 1	Yr 2	Yr 3	Yr 4	Yr 5	Yr 6	Yr 7	Yr 8	Yr 9	Yr 10
Tangible										
Asset uptime		10	20	30	30	30	30	30	30	30
Material cost (Work)		10	20	30	30	30	30	30	30	30
Inventory Value		5	10	15	15	15	15	15	15	15
Labor										
Planning & Scheduling		5	15	20	20	20	20	20	20	20
Inventory & Purchasing		5	10	20	20	20	20	20	20	20
Overtime	5	10	15	15	15	15	15	15	15	15
Absenteeism	5	5	5	5	5	5	5	5	5	5
Capital Projects		5	7	7	7	7	7	7	7	
Energy Costs		5	10	10	10	10	10	10	10	10
Paper	20	30	40	40	40	40	40	40	40	40
Continuous Improvement (O&M)			5	5	5	5	5	5	5	5

Direct Costs

Consulting Costs to Design and Implement the AM Program

Many companies feel that they are incapable of managing an asset management program due to lack of specific expertise, availability of resources and the need to focus on the core work on a day-to-day basis. Often, such companies turn to consulting firms for help. The cost of these services has to be accounted for, which may include the design, piloting, rollout and overall support of the AM program.

People Effectiveness Components of the AM Program

New ways of working will require changes to the organizational structure, new roles and responsibilities and associated new skills for employees. The cost of organizational design, union negotiations, recruiting, and training must be considered in the program.

Comprehensive Condition Audit

A detailed audit of all assets must be carried out in order to understand the extent of investment needed to bring assets back to their desired performance and reliability or quantify what needs to be modified or replace. This audit will be the driver for the capital program.

Enabling Integrated Technology Solution

Technology is a major component of any asset management program—software and hardware are key enablers of automation, elimination of redundant activities through electronic transactions, capture storage, and the use of key data to support decisions around the asset lifecycle.

Business Applications (Software) Licensing Costs

Software vendors profit by licensing their products. These licenses are usually based on the number of concurrent users that are signed on and using the product. If the company has a large enough user base, it may qualify for a site license. A site license requires the company to pay for licenses up to a specific number (this can vary by vendor from 100 to 500), with any additional licenses beyond the site license number at no charge to the company. This is usually an attractive option for companies with a large user base and a high number of plants or divisions. The direct costs associated with the software licenses are paid when they are actually needed and bought.

Hardware and Networking Infrastructure Upgrade Costs

There is usually a major investment in hardware and networking infrastructure to match the requirements of the software server and workstation needs. Upgrades can allow other applications to operate more effectively and provide accessibility. Extra costs are associated with new servers, work stations, upgrading the Local Area Network (LAN), Wide Area Network (WAN), mobile and remote computing requirements.

Business Applications (Software) Implementation

In addition to consulting, other implementation costs must be factored into project costs. These are costs associated with the definition, development and testing of the necessary interfaces to other applications, conversion of existing electronic data, system configuration, testing, documentation, end-user training, and system roll out. These costs are usually paid to the consulting firm and the vendor. This is however, an area that the company can save significant funds if the implementation method employed provides for early transfer of knowledge to internal resources and a reduction on the dependence on consulting support.

Write-off Costs Associated with Existing (But Obsolete) Business Systems

If an existing system is being replaced, the cost associated with writing off this system must be considered in developing the business plan.

Internal Resources

Establishing an asset management program requires significant amounts of time from many employees. Personnel must be involved in developing the vision, mission, road map and business case for asset management. They will also take on a greater role in detailed design, piloting, implementation and support of the program. If they are replaced when they provide their services to the program, the cost of the replacement should be considered. However, many companies are able to do free up the time and services of these individuals for the duration of the project through temporary organization changes and people taking on additional workloads without incurring an extra cost.

Annual Costs Associated with Ongoing Program Support

Labor Costs

New positions will be needed to carry out the revised business processes associated with the asset management program. The positions must be accounted for in terms of annual compensation and benefits. Some of these positions can be directly associated with new organizational units of support for new technologies).

Keeping Current on Latest Asset Design Trends and Relevant Advances in Technology

Staff must stay on top of advances in technologies and trends associated with the particular industry by keeping skills current, attending conferences, and participating in research activities.

Business Application Maintenance and Support Costs

All software vendors provide maintenance and support service for their products to ensure that their clients stay current on the changes in the product and also help with configuration and user-related problems. Support is, however, provided at a cost that varies from 15% to 20% (of the overall product cost) per year after the first year of implementation.

Keeping Current on the Hardware Infrastructure

The annual cost of upgrading the hardware must also be factored in to the overall budget. This can be a small cost if the IT department has a strategic approach to management of the hardware infrastructure.

COST BENEFIT ANALYSIS (DEVELOPING THE BUSINESS PLAN)

There is a significant outlay of precious capital dollars required to fund an asset management program. Usually there is stiff competition for the available capital dollars from people wanting to do other projects. Senior management requires clear information to decide how the available funding can be assigned to maximize the return on investment. While intangible benefits are normally well received and appreciated, senior management and especially the accounting group look for tangible information. The typical information requested is based on project life that can vary from 5 to 10 years. The following is an explanation of the various accounting principles used to determine the economic feasibility of a project:

- Net Present Value (NPV) of the funds—NPV considers the time value of money. The calculation uses an assumed interest rate and calculates what the value of the overall cost and investment money would be in each year of the project.
- Pay Back Period (PBP)—The payback period is the point where the NPV is equal to zero. At this point the overall expenditure equals the savings. Additional savings represent an overall return on investment. Stated differently, after the PBP the investment in effect earns a profit.
- Rate of Return on the Investment (ROI)—ROI is one of the more popular parameters used to evaluate economic feasibility. The investment costs and savings are evaluated at an assumed interest rate, and the ROI is computed over the project life. The ROI can be compared to the return on investment over a similar time frame in a financial institution.

Before the advent of office productivity tools all the above calculations were done manually. Today all spread sheet programs have these formulas available for calculating NPV and ROI. The PBP can be determined where NPV goes to zero or where the graph cuts the X-axis in a graphical plot. Every company has different threshold values for that payback, NPV or ROI at which it is deemed worthwhile to proceed with the project. Table 4.3 gives an example of a cost benefit analysis using an Excel spreadsheet and Figure 4.2 gives a graphical representation of the data in NPV data for each year in the project.

DEVELOP A RISK PROFILE FOR THE AM PROGRAM

An asset management program can be a risky undertaking and it is important the challenges and constraints are clearly defined to aid senior management in their decision-making. It would be wise for the team to

TABLE 4.3. Cost Benefit Analysis for an Asset Management Program.

Cost and Benefits	Year										Total ($)
	1	2	3	4	5	6	7	8	9	10	
Costs											
Direct Costs											
Consulting services	100,000	100,000	25,000	0	0	0	0	0	0	0	225,000
Software licences	100,000	500,000	100,000	0	0	0	0	0	0	0	700,000
Hardware/network-ing infrastructure	100,000	100,000	100,000	0	0	0	0	0	0	0	300,000
Implementation ser-vices	100,000	100,000	25,000	0	0	0	0	0	0	0	225,000
Internal Resources	100,000	100,000	25,000	0	0	0	0	0	0	0	225,000
System write-off	100,000	0	0	0	0	0	0	0	0	0	100,00
Subtotal	600,000	900,000	275,000	0	0	0	0	0	0	0	1,775,000
Annual Costs											
Software											
maintenance	0	80,000	15,000	33,750	33,750	33,750	33,750	33,750	33,750	33,750	331,250
Hardware update	0	0	0	50,000	50,000	50,000	50,000	50,000	50,000	50,000	350,000
Labor support	0	0	0	150,000	150,000	150,000	150,000	150,000	150,000	150,000	1,050,000
Vendor user											
conference	10,000	10,000	10,000	10,000	10,000	10,000	10,000	10,000	10,000	10,000	100,000
Subtotal	10,000	90,000	25,000	243,750	243,750	243,750	243,750	243,750	243,750	243,750	1,831,250
Total Costs	610,000	990,000	300,000	243,750	243,750	243,750	243,750	243,750	243,750	243,750	3,606,250

(continued)

TABLE 4.2 (continued). Cost Benefit Analysis for an Asset Management Program.

Cost and Benefits	Year										Total ($)
	1	2	3	4	5	6	7	8	9	10	
Savings											
Increased production due to asset uptime		50,000	150,000	300,000	300,000	300,000	300,000	300,000	300,000	300,000	2,300,000
Reduced material usage		75,000	150,000	300,000	300,000	300,000	300,000	300,000	300,000	300,000	2,325,000
Reduced inventory value		100,000	150,000	300,000	300,000	300,000	300,000	300,000	300,000	300,000	2,350,000
Reduced labor	50,000	75,000	100,000	200,000	200,000	200,000	200,000	200,000	200,000	200,000	1,625,000
Better management of Capital Projects		50,000	75,000	125,000	125,000	125,000	125,000	125,000	125,000	125,000	1,000,000
Energy savings		50,000	75,000	100,000	100,000	100,000	100,000	100,000	100,000	100,000	825,000
Reduction in paper costs	1,500	3,000	5,000	5,000	5,000	5,000	5,000	5,000	5,000	5,000	44,500
Savings due to ongoing CI projects			100,000	100,000	100,000	100,000	100,000	100,000	100,000	100,000	800,000
Total Savings	51,500	403,000	805,000	505,000	1,186,250	1,186,250	1,186,250	1,186,250	1,186,250	1,186,250	11,269,500
Nett Savings	-558,500	-558,500	-587,000	282,544	1,128,324	1,918,772	2,657,509	3,347,917	4,831,180	6,446,771	7,663,250
NPV	-521,963	-1,034,671	-622,441								
Cum NPV	9,907,489										
ROI	61%										

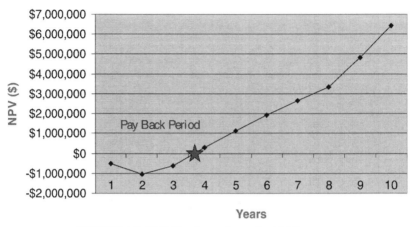

FIGURE 4.2 *NPV Plot for an Attractive AM Program.*

develop a Strength, Weakness, Opportunity and Threats (SWOT) analysis of the proposed program.

Strengths

- Usually very strong economic rationale for carrying out the program.
- Will play well with customers and other stakeholders.
- Will create a safer work place that is more friendly to the environment.
- Structured framework to demonstrate stewardship of the assets in the company.

Weaknesses

- Program costs can be high and securing funds can be difficult if the company has limited access to funds.
- Program life is long and it may be difficult to sustain a high level of commitment throughout the program.
- The program requires a high level of involvement of staff at all levels in the company—securing commitment from these staff to the program could be problematic.

- This program requires change on a large scale impacting almost every department in the company. Effective change management will be crucial to successful and timely implementation.

Opportunities

- Has the potential for sustainability and longevity of the company.
- Increased agility and competitiveness in the marketplace.
- Potential to be a company that is considered best in class in asset management.
- Create a great work environment that will help attract and retain employees who enjoy working for your company.

Threats

- Staff may be unwilling to give up old behaviors especially if it involves dismantling of empires, working harder, and taking on more responsibility.
- Labor unions may not buy in to the program and could slow down implementation.
- Shareholders may be interested in short term profits and may not support an extensive program.

There are number of other issues, concerns and challenges that people should be aware of and know how to deal with when considering the design and implementation of an AM Program. These are discussed in detail in Chapters 12 and 13.

PREPARING A WINNING PROPOSAL TO SENIOR MANAGEMENT

Having completed the cost benefit and SWOT analyses, the next major task is to prepare a winning proposal to senior management. In the example given in Table 4.3 and Figure 4.2, it is obvious that the investment in time and money is very profitable.. However, profit alone may not be enough to sell the project. The team must identify the tangible as well as the intangible benefits. In addition, the challenges listed above should be clearly defined, so that senior management can properly assess the benefits, costs, and risks associated with the project. There should be a clear demonstration by the team that they understand what is involved in the project and are prepared and capable of managing the various activities associated with the project and the roles of the various internal and external players. All of this data should be pulled together in a presentation that is simple, concise and flows smoothly from slide to slide. Presentation software (available in office productivity tools) and data projection system can go a long way to show that the team is willing to embrace technology and are capable of doing a great job. It is usually a good idea for the team to practice and have their sponsor critique the presentation in advance. Open enthusiasm and excitement can demonstrate how passionate the team is about the project.

APPENDIX 4.1—QUESTIONS AND TOPICS FOR HIGH LEVEL ASSESSMENT (FOCUS ON O&M)

1.0 Assets

1.1 Describe what you understand by the term asset management.

1.2 What is your overall view of the condition of the assets you are responsible for?

1.3 Are you given the opportunity to provide input into the design, creation, and commissioning of new assets?

1.4 How do you access information on all of the assets you are responsible for—operations and maintenance?

1.5 Is the information easily available, and where is it stored?

1.6 What input do you have in asset upgrade, modification, and replacement type decisions?

1.7 Do you participate in developing budgets for asset management and how is this done?

1.8 How is the coordination with other groups when this is necessary to work on assets?

1.9 What technology assets do you use to do your work and are they helpful to you?

1.10 Do you leverage asset related data to drive repair/replacement type decisions?

2.0 People

2.1 Describe briefly what you do in the O&M group related to asset management?

2.2 Do you have the right skills and training to do your job effectively?

2.3 Do you feel that you have all the information needed to be effective at your job?

2.4 Describe the communication process in the O&M group at it relates to you?

2.5 Do you feel empowered to identify solutions to problems and raise them to senior management?

2.6 Describe the level of team work in the O&M group.

2.7 How do you know you are doing a good job?

2.8 What performance metrics do you use to support this?

2.9 Do you feel that the experience and knowledge you bring is valued by the O&M group?

2.10 Describe the leadership style of your manager/supervisor.

2.11 Is the current organizational arrangement (locations, teams, job descriptions etc.) effective for getting the job done on the assets?

2.12 How are conflicts and issues managed internally and with support groups?

2.13 Are there service level agreements that govern your relationship with other internal groups?

3.0 Processes

3.1 How would you describe the work processes on assets—reactive, proactive, or optimized?

3.2 Describe how you are assigned your daily work.

3.3 Describe how work is planned and scheduled.

3.4 How effective is the materials management process?

3.5 How effective is the customer service process?

3.6 How do you interface with the customer and is this relationship what it should be?

3.7 Do you get all the information you need in order to do your job effectively?

3.8 Do you have all the needed tools and equipment to do a good job?

3.9 Do you get involved in the budgeting process and if so what is your role?

3.10 What is your perception of "wrench on bolt time" in the O&M group?

3.11 Are contractors used to do work and how do you interact with them?

APPENDIX 4.2—KEY ELEMENTS OF A TEAM CHARTER

(1) Team name

(2) Project name

(3) Listing of team members

(4) Project mandate—vision and objectives

(5) Authority of the team members

(6) Scope—key activities, timeframes and costs

(7) Results—deliverables and milestones

(8) Accountabilities to various groups for listed items

(9) Relationships with other groups (what they provide to your team and what you provide to them related to the project)

(10) Issue and conflict management process

APPENDIX 4.3—COMMUNICATION PLAN

Communication Plan Elements

Stakeholders (Who needs to hear it)	Message (What needs to be conveyed)	Objectives (Why do they need to know)	Implementation			
			Who does it	When	How	How Often

CHAPTER 5

Strategies for Sustainable Asset Management

STRATEGIES FOR SUSTAINABLE ASSET MANAGEMENT

The traditional approach to managing a business has been very siloed and thus an overarching strategy for managing assets over their lifecycle does not exist. For a company to be sustainable, it must practice effective asset management to continue to provide goods and services that keep customers happy and willing to buy again and again. In many companies, organizational structure itself is a major constraint to making the best use of its resources and to eliminating redundancies in business processes. Organizational design and effectiveness have been explored by pioneers in the field. These concepts focus on coordination, communication, empowerment and delegation but fail to address the organization's relationship to assets and to business processes. Similarly, firms have redesigned business processes and introduced automation but have failed to get the desired results. To move your company's business past the medium term and into the long term, it is essential to embrace the concept that all three components need to be developed together—assets, people and processes. Figure 5.1 provides a graphical representation of this idea.

Effective asset management requires strategies in all three areas—assets, people, and processes. Each individual strategy must be valid for the different stages of the asset lifecycle. In addition, the strategies must be flexible in dealing with changes in the business environment in which the asset exists. That is, the company must be able to survive demand fluctuations, the introduction of new technologies, people-related

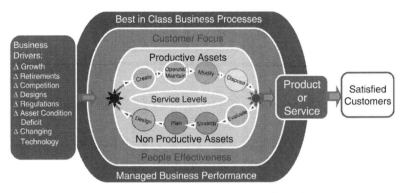

FIGURE 5.1 *Relationship Among Assets, People, and Processes.*

drivers (new skills, retirements, compensation etc.), and revised or new regulations.

Sustainable asset management requires a shift in strategies. It is apparent that traditional behaviors and thinking will not help your company successfully navigate the changing business environment. Figure 5.2 shows the shift to five new strategies for achieving and maintaining a high level of performance in the area of asset management.

Strategy 1—Effective Coordination Around the Asset Lifecycle

Everyone in the company must understand the asset lifecycle phases, be competent in executing their role for the phase they are responsible for, and understand the coordination needs of the other lifecycle phases.

Strategy 2—Match the Asset Mix to the Demand Needs of Customers and Changing Technology Trends

Understand the changing business environment, technology trends, and customer needs. Ensure that the asset mix (productive and non-productive) is managed proactively to meet these needs.

Strategy 3—Develop a High-Performance Organization with a Culture of Continuous Improvement

A high-performance organization of motivated staff with the right skills and knowledge to create new assets, and also operate and maintain the company's existing asset mix to produce a good or service for a satisfied customer and continuously looking at ways to be more effective in this process.

Strategy 4—Effective (Right Tasks Done at the Right Time) Business Processes for All Phases of the Asset Lifecycle.

Re-engineer all business processes for each phase of the asset lifecycle to eliminate non-value- added steps, have the right steps done at the right time, ensuring coordination requirements are achieved through service level agreements; roles, responsibilities, and performance targets are clear and understood.

Strategy 5—Proactively Initiate Change to Effectively Meet Business Drivers

Continuously scan the business environment, identify relevant changes, drivers that affect the asset, people, and process elements and adjust strategies and tactics in these areas.

Sustainable Asset Management Requires a Shift in Strategies

Asset Life Cycle Managed in Silos to Effective Coordination Over the Asset Life Cycle

Asset Mix Driven by Demand Needs Only to Supply/Demand Analysis

Dysfunctional Organization to High Performance Organization

Ineffective Business Processes to Re-engineered value added processes

React to change to Proactively initiate change based on business drivers

FIGURE 5.2 Sustainable Asset Management Requires Changes in Behaviors.

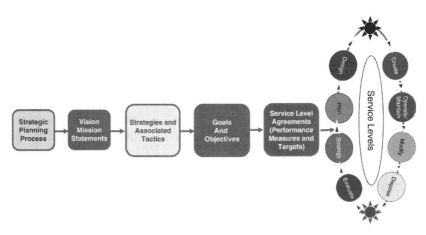

FIGURE 5.3 Strategic Planning Sets the Stage for Effective Coordination Around the Asset Lifecycle.

DETAIL DISCUSSION AND REVIEW OF EACH STRATEGY

Strategy 1—Effective Coordination Around the Asset Lifecycle

Everyone in the company must understand the asset lifecycle phases, be competent in executing their role for the phase they are responsible for, and understand the coordination needs of the other lifecycle phases.

Poor or ineffective coordination of work (tasks, activities) around the asset lifecycle is possibly the number one reason why organizations fail to realize the full value from their business operations. Designing for effective coordination starts at the strategic planning process. There must be clear direction for asset management in the company's vision and mission statements. Subsequent strategies, associated tactics, goals, objectives and performance measures should all provide the direction to staff that are required to execute business processes in the various phases of the asset lifecycle. This concept is depicted in Figure 5.3.

The organization's strategic plan will yield a vision and mission statement for the company (or an updated one if the company already has one). The vision statement should identify the importance of assets in delivering a high-quality service or product to a customer. The mission statement will show the link among assets, people and processes in achieving the vision and must also be clear on what is required for sustaining the vision. Requirements will be developed as strategies for change, and each of these strategies will have associated tactics for implementation. Goals and objectives for each strategy will be distilled into performance targets and measures, usually within a performance management framework (e.g., balanced scorecard). This dictates what is needed and the level of performance required for the different resources that work in the various business units responsible for executing the asset lifecycle business processes. Many organizations formalize these measures into service-level agreements. In this way they ensure everyone is clear on what is expected from their business unit and what they need to provide to other business units in order for all to be effective in doing their jobs.

Strategy 2—Match the Asset Mix to Demand Needs of Customers and Changing Technology Trends

Understand the changing business environment, technology trends, and customer needs. Ensure that the asset mix (productive and non-productive) is managed proactively to meet these needs.

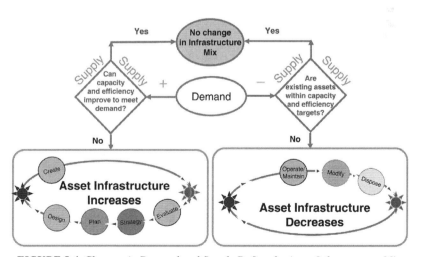

FIGURE 5.4 *Changes in Demand and Supply Define the Asset Infrastructure Mix.*

A major dilemma for many companies is predicting demand and determining the asset mix necessary to effectively produce the product or service in a timely manner. If demand is properly understood, then subsequent modeling of the supply side can reveal if the existing asset mix can meet demand projections.

Demand-side modeling requires a good understanding of customer needs for existing products, new product development, and projected demand for new products. Supply-side modeling requires an understanding of the current asset conditions, capacities, and operating efficiencies. Poor practices in demand-side and supply-side modeling can result in over-investment in the asset mix when existing assets have untapped capacity. It can also result in too little investment and loss of market share because of inability to meet demand.

Changes in the existing asset mix may be driven by factors other than customer needs. Many times, changes in technology, engineering designs and regulations can cause existing assets to be incapable of meeting the performance standards expected. Any company that is not vigilant in scanning the business environment to identify these trends early can be caught with obsolete and inefficient assets or assets that cannot meet changing regulations. This can spell the end for some companies and may mean significant loss in market share (e.g., certain companies did not move fast enough to embrace the plasma television or digital cameras technologies).

In order for projections of the asset mix to be made it is obvious that planners must have reliable information on the condition, capacity, efficiency and reliability of existing assets. They must be aware of the level of obsolescence of the existing assets and the availability of more advanced and cost-effective assets. Similarly, operations and maintenance staff must consistently strive to keep assets at target reliability, efficiency and capacity levels with a minimum of redundancy through best in class business processes. Engineering, operations and maintenance must also work together to replace assets when they are no longer economical to operate and modify or upgrade them to accommodate new regulations, safety requirements, squeeze out more capacity or de-bottleneck to gain more capacity. The business processes associated with these concepts will be reviewed in detail in Chapter 6.

Strategy 3—Develop a High-Performance Organization with a Culture of Continuous Improvement

A high-performance organization of motivated staff with the right skills and knowledge needed to create new assets, operate, and maintain the company's existing asset mix to produce a good or service for a satisfied customer and continuously looking at ways to be more effective in this process.

A high-performance organization elicits the best from people who manage assets. How do you develop and sustain a high-performance organization? How do you recognize a high-performance organization? Even if you are able to define what a high-performance organization means, the task of creating one is the challenge. High-performing organizations require change—something that few people have learnt to embrace and live with. Figure 5.5 provides an overview of the main focus areas necessary for a high-performance organization.

High performance starts with an understanding of the company's corporate vision and mission. Organization design principles will help decide organization structure based on:

(1) *The division of labor*—the degree of work specialization necessary to carry out the business processes around the asset lifecycle.

(2) *Distribution of authority*—degree of centralization necessary for

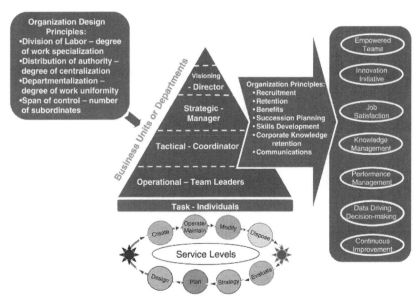

FIGURE 5.5 *A High-Performance Organization is Essential for People to be Effective in Asset Management.*

coordination of work, allowing room for flexibility but still providing the corporate oversight needed for high standards and consistency.

(3) *Departmentalization*—degree of work uniformity and the logical grouping of activities together.

(4) *Span of control*—the number of subordinates necessary to effectively execute the assigned activities.

The assets necessary to create the product or service, the available work force and the unique business processes required to create and manage the asset mix constitute the operating business environment. When the above four organization design principles are applied, managers can determine the unique business units or departments needed to effectively coordinate and execute the activities around the asset lifecycle. Within each business unit, the various roles, levels of authority and responsibility, together with the number of employees, will be decided.

Having laid the foundation for an effective organization, you can get the best from people only by practicing sound organizational principles:

- *Recruitment*—hiring the right people for the job.
- *Retention*—retaining these people and helping them succeed within the company.
- *Benefits and compensation*—create a win-win situation, allow staff to be able to create wealth also.
- *Skills Development*—understand the skills needed to do each job competently, understand the skills of your staff and help them to develop the skills needed to be effective as well as those needed to move up in the organization.
- *Succession Planning*—plan for the eventual departure of staff from the organization through natural attrition and for other reasons.
- *Corporate Knowledge Retention*—ensure that all the knowledge required to be world-class at asset management and in fact to be competitive and successful in your business is captured, stored and shared for continuity for the organization (leverage technology).
- *Communications*—practice all-way communication, ensure that everyone knows what they need to know to do their job effectively, create an environment that encourages open and honest discussion.

- *Rewards and Recognition*—reap the benefits from a motivated workforce with the right attitudes by rewarding good work and initiative.

How do you recognize a high-performance organization? Such an organization will demonstrate behaviors consistent with:

- Empowered teams
- Innovation and initiative
- High level of job satisfaction—right attitude, high motivation
- Knowledge management
- Performance management
- Continuous improvement
- Use of data to drive decision making
- Partnering with labor unions to solve people issues and conflicts

Strategy 4—Effective (Right Tasks Done at the Right Time) Business Processes for All Phases of the Asset Lifecycle.

Re-engineer all business processes for each phase of the asset lifecycle to eliminate non-value added steps, have the right steps done at the right time, ensuring coordination requirements are achieved through service-level agreements; roles, responsibilities, and performance targets are clear and understood.

The re-engineering process is shown in Figure 5.6 . It starts with a listing of the business processes currently carried out around the asset

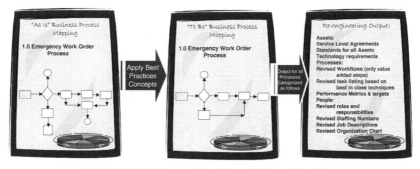

FIGURE 5.6 *Process Mapping and Re-engineering.*

lifecycle. It is important to map out the way work is done in these processes and identify the tasks, hand-offs to people, roles and responsibilities, current staffing numbers and service-level agreements, if they exist. When the process mapping is complete, you will now be in a position to determine what business processes are necessary.

Re-engineering business processes requires thoughtful reflection, facilitation by an expert, and the application of best-in-class concepts to determine the most effective way of performing the processes. Best-in-class concepts will be discussed in detail in Chapter 6. When these concepts are applied, the resulting workflows are simplified as much as possible by eliminating non-valued-added steps. There will be outputs from the re-engineering process that must be implemented to achieve improvements (discussed in detail in Chapter 12). They include:

(1) Assets:
    (a) Service-level agreements
    (b) Standards for all assets
    (c) Technology requirements
(2) Processes:
    (a) Revised workflows (only value-added steps)
    (b) Revised task listing based on best-in-class techniques
    (c) Performance metrics & targets
(3) People:
    (a) Revised roles and responsibilities
    (b) Revised staffing numbers
    (c) Revised job descriptions
    (d) Revised organization chart

Strategy 5—Proactively Initiate Change to Effectively Meet Business Drivers

Continuously scan the business environment, identify relevant changes, drivers that affect the asset, people and process elements, and adjust strategies and tactics in these areas.

Many companies have found that improving performance can be done through implementation of new concepts, re-engineering their business processes, and enabling technology solutions. Organizations have found that this was the easy part of the change process. Sustaining a high level of performance and continuously improving as the business environment

Sustainability is About Becoming and Staying Competitive

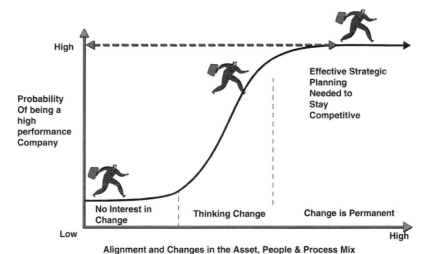

FIGURE 5.7 *Sustainability. Becoming and Staying Competitive.*

Sustainability-Focused Strategic Planning

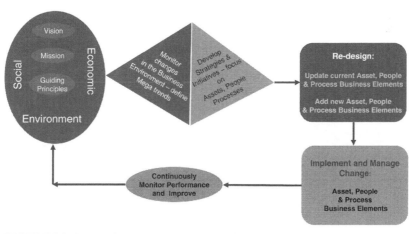

FIGURE 5.8 *Sustainability Focused Strategic Planning Enables Competitiveness In the Asset, People and Process Areas.*

73

changes is the key differentiator of best-in-class companies. Figure 5.7 shows that radical re-engineering in the assets, people, and business process areas is necessary to become competitive. Sustainability is about becoming and staying competitive and requires effective strategic planning with a high level of alignment of assets, people, and processes. Figure 5.8 depicts the basic elements of the strategic planning process and starts from a clear definition and understanding of a company's vision, mission and guiding principles. These must be based on the triple bottom line—social, economic, and environmental. The company's vision must demonstrate how the company wants to be seen by the community in which they operate in these three areas. The company's mission and guiding principles will define how they intend to get there. Effective strategic planning in the asset management area requires constant monitoring of the business environment to identify drivers for change (e.g., changes in regulations, technology, skill sets of people etc.). Strategies with their linked tactics and performance targets should then be developed in the assets, people, and processes areas to deal effectively with these drivers for change. The standard business transformation process of re-design, implement change and continuously manage performance closes the loop.

CHAPTER 6

Leading Asset Management Practices

LEADING ASSET MANAGEMENT PRACTICES

Asset management practices, like many in business, are focused on accomplishing a specific task or activity through specific behaviors. When these behaviors produce desired results and are consistent with leading thinking in the asset management field, they are referred to as leading (or best or world-class) practices. Each practice can be viewed on a continuum from the one extreme of being totally undesirable (causing major negative consequences) to the other extreme of being viewed as world class, i.e., exhibiting excellence in all regards. There are clear phases along this continuum that you must attain before you can get to the excellence level. In a simplistic form, the continuum can be converted to a quantitative scale (see Figure 6.1).

Understanding where you are on this scale for asset management practices is critical in determining the opportunity gap and sets the stage for re-engineering (if radical change is needed) or process improvement (if incremental change is needed). You should not be surprised to find that your organization may be doing some of these practices already. It is generally very easy to identify these practices; it is not so easy to determine where you lie on the continuum. This can be due to lack of knowledge of what the best-practice version looks like, lack of reliable data to make the assessment, or a reluctance to accept reality. A clear description of what each level means for each practice is a fundamental step in the journey towards a best-in-class asset management program. This would provide a roadmap for implementation, where progress in changing to desired behaviors can be checked on an ongoing basis. In addition, it is important to

Practices Rating Scale

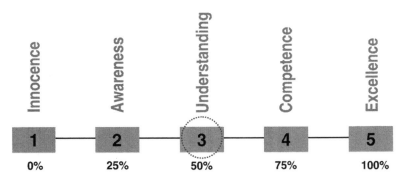

FIGURE 6.1 *Practices Rating Scale.*

understand that these practices must work in concert to deliver optimal results. Asset management practices can be categorized into two major areas: general practices that can be applied around the entire asset lifecycle and practices that are unique to a specific lifecycle phase.

General Asset Management Practices

- Strategic Planning
- Performance Management
- Risk Management
- Financial management
- Capital Project Planning and Execution
- Corporate Knowledge Retention
- Organization Effectiveness

Asset Management practices unique to the lifecycle phase

- Needs identification and planning—demand- and supply-side management concepts.
- Design review of best in class process for doing asset design.
- Procurement and construction.
- Commissioning—ensuring that O&M gets the best chance to effectively operate and maintain when the switch goes "on."
- O&M—review of best in class &M concepts:
  —Program driven work

—Materials Management—focusing on the inventory process
—Predictive maintenance
—Reliability centered maintenance
—Operations management
—Energy management

- Upgrade/modify—concepts around decision making with respect to asset modification and upgrade decision and the execution process.
- Decommission or take out of service—recommendations on how to make this a value-added and safe process.

GENERAL ASSET MANAGEMENT PRACTICES

Strategic Planning

Strategic planning is the determination of the basic long-term goals and objectives of the enterprise in line with the triple bottom line (social, economic and environmental), adoption of the course of action, and allocation of resources for carrying out these goals.

Strategic planning is a complex activity that a company must undertake in order to be proactive about dealing with the issues that continuously challenge survival. These include: profitability, growth in sales, market share, operating costs, competitive position, pricing, environmental scanning, human resource management, shareholder value. All companies should have a strategic plan that looks forward for at least five years. This plan should be updated annually and should be the focus of a major review every three years. The strategic planning process (Figure 6.2) is the first step on the way to effective asset management. The company's vision and mission statements and guiding principles epitomize the economic, social, and environmental aspects of the business environment and reflect how everyone (public, shareholders, employees, regulators) should perceive the company. The company's vision, mission, and guiding principles must take into account the key elements of asset management—assets, people and processes. In addition, world-class companies ensure that the concept of sustainability is considered in the strategic planning process. (Sample vision, mission & guiding principles are shown in Appendix 6.1). Once the vision, mission, and guiding principles have been finalized, the stage is set for identification of strategies to achieve the vision and mission in the face of changes in the business environment. It is essential here that good scanning of the business environment be carried out to identify mega trends and business

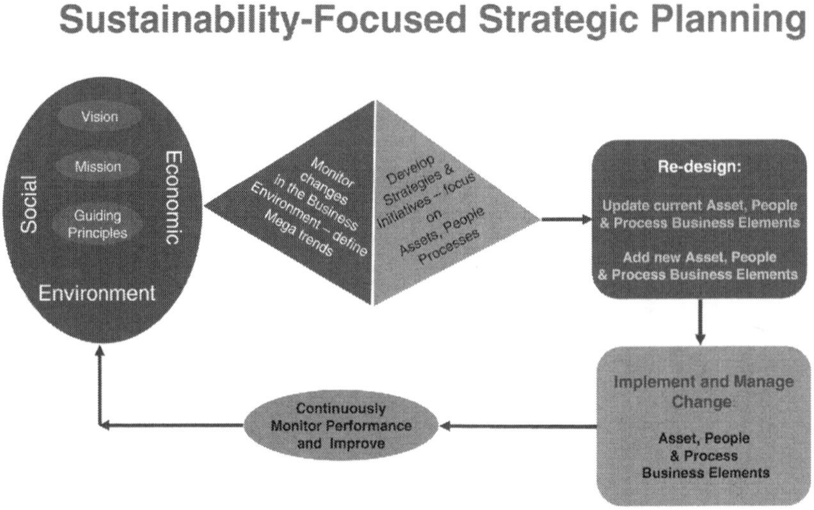

Sustainability-Focused Strategic Planning

FIGURE 6.2 *Strategic Planning Focusing on Assets, People and Processes*

drivers for change. Existing strategies may need to be updated and new strategies defined together with associated tactics to meet and deal effectively with change. The redesign and implementation phases are necessary steps in the business transformation process to enable the various strategies. All successful companies understand that the strategic planning process is ongoing. They continuously monitor performance and seek different ways to sustain a high level of performance. This is a necessary step in closing the strategic planning loop.

Strategic Planning Deliverables

- History map (that can be posted at key company functions) to remind staff how we got to where we are.
- Drivers for change (social, economic, environmental).
- Updated company vision, mission statements, high-level mandate for change and high-level strategies for change.
- Opportunity gaps, choices—detailed strategies for change.
- Detailed implementation plans for each strategy. Strategies implemented with associated performance tracking, support and culture change plan.
- Ongoing environmental scanning, performance management in line with strategic targets, and continuous improvement initiatives.

Performance Management

The old saying "What gets measured gets done" may be simplistic but has real meaning in the business environment. The best of strategic plans and intentions can amount to very little unless there are clear goals, objectives, and associated targets to ensure that strategies for success are being achieved. Setting targets that are realistic and managing performance and expectations around these targets is essentially the practice of performance management. The balanced scorecard approach (Figure 6.3), modified to fit the philosophy of optimization through assets, people and processes, is a robust framework for performance management.

Performance Management Using the Balanced Scorecard Approach

Financial (Return on Assets)
Succeed financially by Maximizing the Return On Your Assets

Processes
The Right Business Processes At The Right Time All Steps Value-Added

Vision & Mission

Customers
Alignment of Expectations of Customers both Internal and External

People (learning & Growth)
Sustainability of the Workforce – Ability to Change and Improve

FIGURE 6.3 *Performance Management Using the Balanced Scorecard.*

The balanced scorecard framework, performance is managed in four key areas:

- *Customers*—how do we want our external customers to see the company in the areas of quality, cost, responsiveness, social and environmental.
- *Financial*—overall return on all assets employed in the production of goods or services. We must be able to visualize how we must appear to our shareholders or the public if we are succeeding financially.
- *People*—are our people learning and growing with us, are we developing agility and flexibility necessary to change and continuously improve?
- *Processes*—to satisfy our customers (both internal and external), what processes should we excel at and how do we know that we are excelling at these processes?

Performance management is closely associated with the strategic planning process discussed above. The following are the main links to the strategic planning process:

- During the visioning step, a corporate scorecard is developed for the various strategies that are critical to the success of the company.
- This is distilled further with the input of a wide cross-section of staff at the business unit level to create the business unit level scorecard.
- Further refinement to the frontline team level results in simple team scorecards that are tied directly to corporate goals and objectives.
- Monitoring, trending, feedback and adjustments to plans support your vision of sustainability.

Deliverables when implementing a performance management program:

- Corporate balanced scorecard
- Business Units balanced scorecards
- Frontline Teams balanced scorecards
- Technology solution for creating, tracking and managing the respective metrics
- Training on performance management

Risk Management

Risk management is a complex business process that is often over-looked or poorly practiced. The advent of terrorism on a global scale has suddenly brought risk management to the forefront. Many companies have completed vulnerability assessments or are in the process of doing so. Unfortunately, this is the extent of risk management that most companies undertake. Successful companies apply risk managment to many areas of their operations and in particular their capital projects program. When risk management is focused on the triple bottom line (economic, social and environmental), companies experience enhanced profit, environmental performance and the communities in which they operate also benefit. At a tactical level, risk management is a key process in asset management providing input for decision-making in the areas of new assets being considered, modifications and upgrades to existing assets replacement of existing assets and taking existing assets out of service. The scope of business risk is broad and can arise from a range of sources[4]—the key areas are as follows:

- *Strategic risk*—this is the risk of planning failure, e.g., poor marketing and acquisition, strategies, failure to anticipate political or regulatory change.
- *Financial risk*—this is risk of failure of financial control, e.g., systemic failure, poor receivables and inventory management, funding of the capital program.
- *Operational risk*—this is the risk of human actions, either willful or by omission, e.g., system mistakes, design oversights, unsafe practices, sabotage.
- *Commercial risk*—this the risk of business interruption e.g. loss of key personnel, failure of the supply chain, legal and compliance issues.
- *Technical risk*—this is the risk of failure of physical assets, e.g,, equipment failure, infrastructure breakdown, fire and physical impact, explosion and/or sabotage, pollution or natural events.

The major elements of a risk management process are given in Figure 6.4.

---

[4]Triple Bottom Line Risk Management by Adrian R. Bowden, Malcolm R. lane, Julia H. Martin published by John Wiley & Sons, 2001.

Major Elements of Risk Analysis

FIGURE 6.4 *Major Elements of Risk Management.*

- *Step 1*—the process starts off by setting the framework by defining the—objectives of risk management
- *Step 2*—is to identify the risks specific to the business area, strategy or project—questions such as *"what might occur?"* and *"how might they occur?"* need to be answered.
- *Step 3*—evaluating the risks developing probabilities that the particular event may occur, the consequences of occurrence and ranking the risk in order of importance.
- *Step 4*—treatment of the risks identified, identifying various options for mitigation of the risk events, development of implementation plans and subsequent implementation of these plans.

Deliverables from a risk management process for a particular focus area are as follows:

- Definition risk events with associated probabilities of occurrence and consequences and ranking in order of importance or significance.

- Listing of mitigation options and evaluation of alternatives for the associated risk event.
- Implementation plans for the mitigation action chosen and the deliverables associated with implementation.

Financial Management

Figure 6.5 displays all of the important outside cash transactions which a company regularly undertakes. There are five key groups or stakeholders that are involved in the cash transactions:

(1) *Customers*—those who pay cash into the corporation in return for goods and services provided by the company.
(2) *Employees*—individuals paid for the time and work they sell to the corporation.

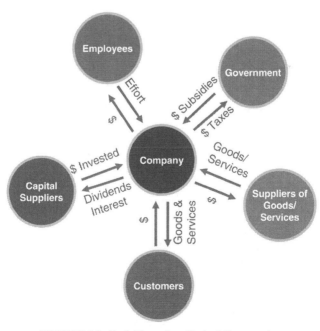

FIGURE 6.5 *Cash Flows in a Typical Corporation.*

(3) *Government*—public institution that is paid taxes and renders subsidies to the corporation.

(4) *Suppliers of goods and services to the corporation*—those who sell the raw materials, MRO spares, machines, land, expert advice etc. that the company uses in its ongoing operations.

(5) *Capital suppliers*—investors that give cash to the company in return for dividends, interest payments, or other future cash flow.

The company is therefore an entity accepting goods and services from employees and vendors and paying for those services with cash. The company operates those assets to produce goods and services that it provides to customers who in turn pay for them in cash. The company also pays taxes and receives subsidies from the government. The company raises cash from capital suppliers to acquire productive capacity, while servicing those capital claims with cash interest payments, principal payments and dividends. The company relies on its capital suppliers to provide the cash necessary for it to accomplish its productive plans, such as investments in new assets, upgrades and modifications or simply to keep its head above water for one more period. In other words, the company needs to manage its finances in order to execute its asset management plans! If the company gets it wrong in any of the five areas identified above, it can end up with severe or life- threatening cash-flow problems. The goal of financial management is to maximize the cash inflows and ensure that cash outflows all create value to the company. One aspect of maximizing cash inflow is project funding. Selecting capital suppliers that offer attractive options is a key part of this process, as is ensuring that projects are properly evaluated using standard economic criteria. It means that everyone making demands on the company's cash flows should have clear and justifiable reasons for the capital requested. This can be normal operating budgets or capital requests for new assets or upgrades and modifications to existing assets. It is therefore important that proper that economic analyses be carried out for all projects. The decision to move forward with projects must be based on clear economic criteria such as Net Present Value, Internal Rate of Return on Investment, and Payback Period. As discussed in Chapter 4.

Capital Projects Planning and Execution

Is your capital program focusing on the right areas for competitiveness and sustainability? Most capital programs are high-dollar value and usually are funded to the detriment of operations and maintenance needs.

When the projects that get into the capital program are not carefully evaluated and prioritized, it is possible that badly needed funds get allocated to low-priority or non-value added areas. The capital program is the heart of the asset renewal process. Project requests can be initiated from various areas of the asset lifecycle—the demand/supply side analysis, modifications or upgrades, asset replacement, or asset decommissioning. There are four steps to the capital projects process:

- *Step 1*—Identification of projects. It is important to develop a process for new projects from the four areas identified above that ensures consistency in all capital project requests that are created.
- *Step 2*—All project requests should have an accompanying business case that clearly identifies costs, benefits (tangible/intangible) and economic indicators such as Net Present Value, Return on Investment and Pay Back Period.
- *Step 3*—All requests should then be evaluated and prioritized for approval of funding.
- *Step 4*—Projects should then be executed using the standard project management cycle[5]—Initiation, Planning, Controlling, Executing and Closing.

Figure 6.6 shows the initiation step from the asset lifecycle followed by the project management process.

All projects require careful attention to the various practices within each phase of the project lifecycle, and each starts with the creation of the right project team. Successful project management requires the following: Integration of Project Tracks, Management of—Scope, Time, Cost, Quality, Human Resources, Risk, Procurement, Communications, Issues and Conflicts, Benefits tracking and effective management of the impact of the project on existing operations.

Capital Projects deliverables based on the above process are:

- Capital project initiation standards.
- Solid business case/benefits tracking framework.
- Project management deliverables—team charter, communications plan, project plan/detailed project schedule, regular progress reports, meeting minutes, updated schedule showing earned value.
- Asset standards for procurement/construction.

[5]Project Management Body Of Knowledge (PMBOK).

Capital Projects Planning & Execution

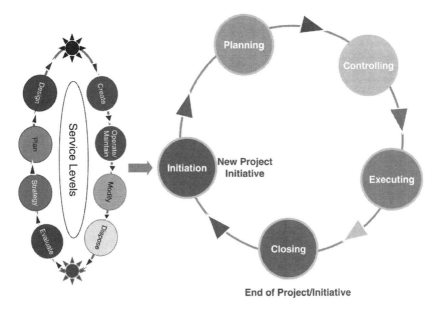

FIGURE 6.6 *Capital Projects Process.*

Corporate Knowledge Retention

Corporate knowledge is the collective wisdom that keeps a company competitive, high performing, and innovative. Corporate knowledge is one of the building blocks of sustainability. Acquiring the right knowledge, sharing it with those who need to know, and continuously refining that knowledge are fundamental to a high-performance organization. Corporate knowledge is acquired over years and is created and handed down by the people who work in the company. Some companies conduct mergers and acquisitions to increase corporate knowledge and ensure competitiveness and sustainability. Many companies are vulnerable on many fronts in the area of corporate knowledge:

- Knowledge areas are not defined and linked to the company's core business areas.
- Knowledge is not secure and is vulnerable to competitors.
- Knowledge is stored in difficult-to-access media.

- Most of the company's corporate knowledge is stored in people's head—and it walks out when the employee leaves the company.
- There are varying versions of the knowledge, and it is interpreted differently by different groups or individuals.

The knowledge management circle (Figure 6.7) shows how your organization becomes effective at this important process. There are five steps to the knowledge management process:

- *Step 1*—Define knowledge areas. This step is a critical starting point for understanding the business you are in and the knowledge areas you must master.
- *Step 2*—Conduct a knowledge assessment. When knowledge areas are defined, you can conduct an assessment of how well you perform in each of the areas. This opportunity gap then needs to be translated into a business case for implementing a knowledge management program.
- *Step 3*—Analyze, design, and develop an action plan to close any gaps identified. This steps develops all the tactical detail to make knowledge management an effective business process for your company.
- *Step 4*—Implement the action plan to close the gap. This requires the necessary funding, resources and appropriate implementation team to take the action plan to reality.
- *Step 5*—Optimize, keep on creating new knowledge, refine existing knowledge and share knowledge with every one who needs to know to do their job effectively. Ensure that rewards and recognition follow for those who are passionate about knowledge management.

A key aspect of corporate knowledge retention and knowledge management is the huge challenge of managing data in a world swamped with electronic data. Many companies are struggling to manage the deluge of data that has been made possible by the information age. Successful companies have recognized the relationship between data, information, knowledge, and sustainability of their business. They have come to understand what data is relevant to their business, capture it electronically (as far as possible), shape it into information, interpret it based on intellectual capacity, share it with anyone who needs to use it to do their jobs effectively, and continuously refine it as the business environment changes. Figure 6.8 gives a high-level overview of how an integrated technology solution can support corporate knowledge retention.

Knowledge Management (KM)

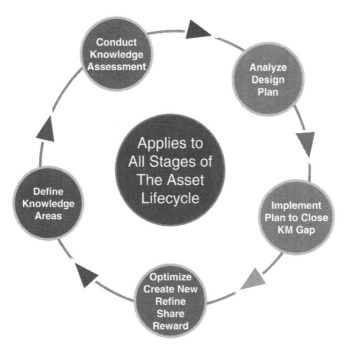

FIGURE 6.7 *Knowledge Management Circle.*

Essentially, the integrated technology asset contributes to business processes, creates data (dynamic and static) and allows for that data to be easily mined, queried, sorted and interpreted to drive decision-making. The integrated technology asset will be discussed in detail in Chapter 8—Enabling Technologies for Asset Management.

Deliverables from a corporate knowledge management program (based on the Knowledge Management Circle):

- *Step 1*—Definition of knowledge areas for business excellence and sustainability.
- *Step 2*—Opportunity gap, choices and business case.
- *Step 3*—Detailed implementation plan to develop an effective KM process and close opportunity gaps.
- *Step 4*—Implementation of KM Process, Integrated Technology Solution, and tracking of results.

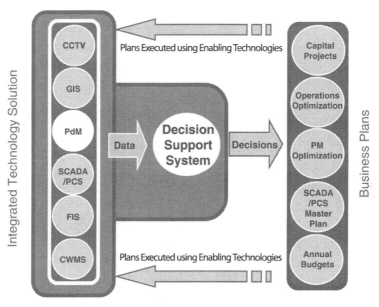

FIGURE 6.8 *Integrated Technology Supports Corporate Knowledge Management.*

- *Step 5*—Culture of knowledge optimization—creating new, refining existing, rewards and recognition for those who actively participate in knowledge management.

Organization Effectiveness

A company's vision and mission statement identify the business they are in and set the stage for the assets necessary to create the service or product for the client base. The combination of assets into various processes and systems will determine the business processes at which the organization must excel to be competitive and a best-in-class organization. The next piece of the puzzle is to look at the people needed to execute the business processes, operating and maintaining the asset mix to satisfy the customer. Achieving organizational effectiveness is probably the most difficult of the three business elements. When done well, it can transform a company into a high-performance organization of world-class stature,

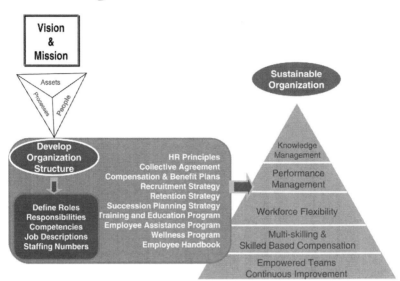

FIGURE 6.9 *Developing a High-Performance Organization.*

which continues to hold that position for many years. When done poorly, moving towards organizational effectiveness can result in a company going out of business. Figure 6.9 shows the steps involved in developing and sustaining a high-performance organization needed to support effective asset management (this process can be applied to existing organizations or building a new organization):

- *Step 1*—Define or validate asset and business process requirements necessary to achieve the company's vision and mission.
- *Step 2*—develop the organization structure needed to execute the business processes on the asset mix to deliver the service or create the product to the customer base. This should be based on design concepts for an organic or mechanistic design based on *division of labor, distribution of authority, departmentalization,* and *span of control* (see Figure 6.10).
- *Step 3*—Define roles, responsibilities, performance standards, skills and competencies. Combine these into the necessary job descriptions that will help you achieve your vision for the organization. Develop staffing numbers for each job description

based on the amount of work to be done in executing the business processes effectively.

- *Step 4*—Develop underlying organizational concepts necessary to nurture and keep the organization operating smoothly. These would include: human resources principles, a collective agreement with your union partner, compensation and benefit plans, recruitment, retention, succession planning strategies, employee assistance and wellness programs, and skills development program.

When the above approach is implemented it is realistic to expect a high-performance organization where people demonstrate the following desired behaviors:

- Knowledge management is actively practiced resulting in corporate knowledge retention.
- Performance management drives effectiveness and decision making.
- The workforce practices workforce flexibility improving "wrench on bolt time."
- The workforce is multi-skilled minimizing the number of personnel needed to do a job safely and effectively.

Organization Design Principles:

FIGURE 6.10 *Organization Design Principles.*

- People work in a team environment and are empowered to be creative, and to identify and execute continuous improvement initiatives that can keep the organization sustainable.

Deliverables from an organizational Effectiveness Program (based on the above methodology):

- *Step 1*—Documentation of asset mix, clear definition of business processes.
- *Step 2*—Organization structure.
- *Step 3*—Documentation of roles, responsibilities, performance standards, skills and competencies, job descriptions and staffing numbers.
- *Step 4*—Human resources principles, collective agreement, compensation and benefit plans, recruitment, retention, succession-planning strategies, employee assistance and wellness programs and skills development program.

ASSET MANAGEMENT PRACTICES UNIQUE TO THE LIFECYCLE PHASE

Demand and Supply Side Management Concept

How do new assets get into the system and how do old assets get out of the system? In practice companies tend to be good at recommending, budgeting for, and creating new assets. Not many companies are as adept at taking old assets with sound economic rationale out of the system. The result is an asset mix that is not effective at delivering the service or product. In other words, there is untapped value in the existing asset mix, which, if fully exploited, could reduce the capital program and free up funds for other important areas of the company's business. Figure 6.11 shows how demand and supply side modeling can help ensure you have the optimal mix of assets at all times. There are three scenarios that need to be considered.

Scenario 1—Increase in Demand for Products or Services

When demand increases, persons responsible for providing the asset capacity to meet that demand should ask a fundamental question—*can the capacity and efficiency of existing assets satisfy the increase in demand?* Answering "no" would mean that O&M staff are doing a

Demand and Supply Modeling
Defines the Asset Mix

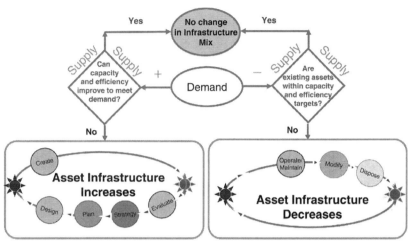

FIGURE 6.11 *Optimal Asset Mix Through Demand- and Supply-Side Modeling.*

world-class job in operating and taking care of these assets and are unable to squeeze any excess capacity from the system. This answer then leads to requests to the capital program for adding new assets to the mix.

If a careful review of the existing asset base is considered and it can be stated that "*yes—capacity and efficiency of existing can be improved to satisfy the increase in demand,*" then the asset base does not change. There may still be requests to the capital program for upgrades and modifications to squeeze out excess capacity. In addition, it can mean introducing best-in-class operations and maintenance practices to improve performance and reliability of the existing asset.

Scenario 2—Decrease in Demand for Products or Services

When there is a decrease in demand (which can be short-term, medium-term, or long-term), those responsible for providing the asset capacity to meet demand should ask a fundamental question—"*are existing assets within capacity and efficiency targets?*" A "yes" answer to this question will result in no change in the asset mix. If the answer is "*no,*" it may mean that there is excess capacity in the system, and it will be necessary to take an asset out of operation for the short term, mothball it if demand is expected to be lower in the medium term, or decommission the asset if the reduced demand is expected to be long term in nature. These actions, again, can result in requests for project work in the capital program.

Scenario 3—Demand Stays Steady

In this situation, demand is relatively steady. Yet, O&M have to face the never-ending task of maximizing capacity and efficiency from assets that follow set deterioration patterns. Supply-side modeling to meet this steady demand will identify projected upgrade, modification and /or replacement requests to the capital projects program. This can be for productive assets or co-productive assets (e.g., technology assets, new tools and equipment), needed to keep the existing assets at the desired level of reliability, efficiency, and capacity.

There are many sophisticated tools that can be employed in the demand-modeling process to determine projected demands for services and products. Similarly, there are tools for evaluating the capacity and efficiency of an existing asset base. Models need to incorporate projected changes in performance and reliability based on standard deterioration curves applicable to the relevant asset type.

Deliverables from Supply/Demand-Modeling

- Projected capacity and efficiency ratings of the existing asset base by defined processes.
- Projected demands for services or products based on marketing techniques.
- Capital project listing for:
  —upgrades and modifications to existing assets
  —mothballing of assets
  —full decommissioning of assets and site restoration
  —new assets to be added to the asset base

Review of Best-in-class Process for Doing Asset Design

Specialized companies exist that design specific assets as products for clients. Companies usually procure various assets from different suppliers and then create a design that meets their client needs. For example, a water treatment plant design may use pumps from one supplier, filter assemblies from another and instrumentation and controls from various suppliers. It is not the intent of this book to provide guidance on design of specific components, but rather provide some pointers on what should be considered in developing a complete system. There are a number of considerations in asset design:

- Overall cost of ownership—while a company may want the best design and possibly the most reliable, usually available funding limits what can be done. However, in the long run, if the overall cost of ownership is considered over the projected life of the asset, it may be possible to justify a more expensive asset that is less costly to maintain and operate.
- Most advanced technology available for the particular service (environmental, energy usage impacts to be considered here).
- Simplicity of design—complex designs tend to have significantly more operations and maintenance needs.
- Automation to minimize people effort, provide tighter control specifications, and allow for fail-safe operations.
- Conduct vulnerability reviews of the design and incorporate measures that would prevent, slow down, and/or alert personnel of deliberate acts of terrorism.
- Design with O&M in mind:
  —Maintainability (ease of maintenance, easy to access for re-pairs)
  —Reliability—proven track record longer mean time between failures compared to the different alternatives being consid-ered
  —Compatibility with existing assets—interchangeability of spares and components
  —Ease of operations—ergonomic designs
- Design with expansion in mind, for example:
  —Leave floor space for additional pumps (if economically feasi-ble)
  —Provide piping connections with appropriate valving for major suction, discharge and manifold systems
  —Ensure that provisions are made for easy upgrade of the electricity system

In other words, design a great asset and at the same time ensure you have given the people who will operate and maintain the asset the best chance of keeping it performing effectively to meet the customer's needs.

Procurement

The procurement business process plays a key role in the asset lifecycle. Procurement is widely used during the asset creation phase, operations, maintenance, upgrade/modification and even at decommissioning, where you get the salvage or residual value from the asset. The purchasing group has a simple mandate—enter into a contract with a reputable supplier to deliver the goods or services as per the user requirements (usually defined in a purchase requisition or tender) as per the company's policies and guidelines. For major capital projects, it may be helpful to include a purchasing representative as part of the project team so that there is complete alignment on the purchasing requirements. The purchasing representative must ensure that the company's policies and guidelines are always adhered to. In addition to meeting the specifications for the asset or component that have been ordered by the end user, it is important that the following end-user needs are considered in selecting the supplier:

- After-sale support from the supplier.
- Warranty support.
- Maintenance repair and overhaul (MRO) spares.
- Operations and maintenance service bulletins.
- Support for upgrades and modifications.
- New designs to meet changing business needs.

The purchasing process for large capital project items tends to be very efficient, and most items go through a quotation process, with clear evaluation criteria to identify and select the best supplier that can fulfill the desired partnership required by the end user. The procurement of goods and services to support operations and maintenance of the asset is more difficult to manage because of the large number of items and end users involved. There can be conflict between O&M and Purchasing, because in the view of O&M, Purchasing seems to buy cheaper and poorer quality items. On the other hand, Purchasing claims to have ordered what was defined in the requisition. In addition O&M wants to have everything in stock, so that they can get materials anytime to support their reactive work processes. By contrast, Purchasing focuses on keeping stocks to a minimum to minimize funds tied up in inventory. Figure 6.12 provides a simple process for ensuring that the end users and Purchasing work towards the common goal of having the right materials available for the job at the right time through proper planning and coordination. When a purchase requisition is developed by O&M (the requisitioner must be clear

Purchasing Process Ensures Materials & Services Availability

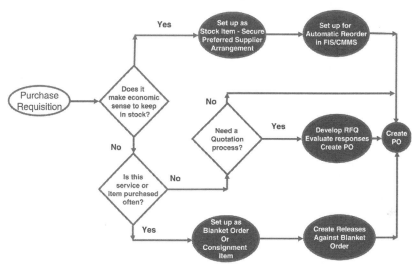

FIGURE 6.12 *Ensuring a Reliable Supply of Materials for O&M.*

on what is required, when and where it should be delivered, cost and appropriate approvals). In the event a preferred supplier is requested, there must be a supporting business case justifying purchase from this supplier.

The purchasing staff should follow the logic suggested in Figure 6.12 to determine if it makes economic sense to stock the item and so ensure the desired service level. In the event that the item does not meet the criteria for stocking but is purchased regularly, it may be possible to set up preferred suppliers with blanket purchase orders that will guarantee timely delivery and after-sales support. The concept of consignment items, where you manage the vendor's stock on your site and pay monthly for any stock that is used is one innovation that supports that "*just in time*" concept of materials management. If the item is an occasional purchase, then it may be necessary to go through a quotation process (high-dollar item or from multiple suppliers) or a direct award to a supplier based on your company's purchasing policies.

Construction or Asset Creation

For simpler assets, the construction process can be simply installation of prefabricated components on a plinth and hook-up of service components (utility lines—electricity, gas, water etc.). Usually, this process is very complex involving many different experts and concurrent activities. Effective project management techniques will ensure that all of these activities are properly coordinated to have the project delivered within the desired timeframe, costs, and minimal impact on existing operations. It is impossible to discuss all the construction techniques for creating an asset. These vary by industry, asset type, and environmental conditions. Below are pointers you should keep in mind during the construction phase of the asset lifecycle that can certainly pay great dividends:

- Develop and implement an effective quality-assurance and control program for ensuring that the proper procedures and materials are being used for construction.
- Provide adequate end user oversight to maximize knowledge transfer and sign off at major milestones. Remember: the site engineer is not an end user. Unfortunately, in many cases a major goal is to complete the project and obtain a completion certificate.
- Inspect all underground asset components before they are covered over—take digital pictures, videos and geo-spatial coordinates (X, Y & Z).
- Do the same for any surface components that will be enclosed and cannot be easily inspected after commissioning.
- Ensure that all underground components are properly protected for corrosion, subsidence and can be located easily through drawings or geo-spatial coordinates.
- Ensure that all vessels are inspected on the inside (where possible) before they are sealed up.
- Keep safety and the environment front and center in everything that is happening on site.
- Observe and document any unique installation requirements for asset components for future reference during the O&M phase.
- Note any engineering design defects and ensure that they are resolved before commissioning. While it is an easier battle to have changes made that are necessary for health, safety and the environment, it is just as important to resolve major O&M issues. If these issues are not resolved, O&M staff will live with the problem for the entire life of the asset—which can be 50 years!

In order for the end user or ultimate owner (operator, maintainer) of the asset to influence the above items, the appropriate participation level and roles must be agreed on at the planning phase.

Commissioning

Commissioning sets the stage for handover of the assets to the owners for ongoing operations and maintenance. Traditionally, commissioning meant ensuring that the individual assets (and the processes they support) performed as per the contract specifications. It also provided an opportunity for celebration, recognition, and general relief that everything went as planned. There is much more that should be obtained from the commissioning phase for engineering/construction, asset component suppliers, operations and maintenance staff:

- Engineering/construction:
    —Validation of the practicality and effectiveness of the design
    —Review of the project management process and lessons for future projects
    —Opportunity to develop better relationships with O&M by offering support during the early life of the asset (infant mortality failures etc.)
- Suppliers:
    —Opportunity to develop relationship with owners, operators and maintainers of the assets
    —Feedback to the company's engineering, research and development groups on design and performance issues that end users would like to see resolved in future designs
- Operations and maintenance
    —Ensure that all asset related data necessary to operate and maintain the asset in the various business applications are in place prior to handover:
    - Computerized Work Management System (CWMS)
    - Asset Management System Database
    - Financial Information System (FIS)
    - Process Control System, SCADA
    - Geographical Information System (GIS)
    - Electronic Document Management System (EDMS—all drawings, specifications, bill of materials, pictures etc.)
    —All baseline information is captured electronically in the asset registry—flows, pressures, speed, voltage, current, vibration, temperature etc. necessary to track the health of the asset. This

would be the ideal performance target—deviations from this would suggest developing problems and the start of asset degradation. Maintenance should be able to plan a suitable intervention to rectify the problem and ensure availability of the asset to the operators.

—All assets are tagged with an asset ID that corresponds to that in the asset registry

—Insurance spares are stored and tracked in the inventory system

—Arrangements have been made with preferred suppliers for re-ordering of MRO spares

—Online operating and troubleshooting manuals are in place

—Operators and maintainers are trained up and competent in performing there respective duties on the asset

—All computer hardware needed to manage the assets (e.g., PCs, laptops, printers, mobile devices) are available in the right quantities and at the appropriate locations

—A contact list of personnel to go to in Engineering, Construction and Suppliers is drawn up and available in the event of problem and issues with asset performance and reliability

O&M—REVIEW OF BEST IN CLASS O&M CONCEPTS

Work Management Process

The work management process is one of the oldest business processes and has been applied in many forms—verbally, on paper, and electronically, using a computerized work management system. Figure 6.13 provides and overview of the various steps in the work management process.

Work Initiation

Work can be initiated in many ways. This can be from equipment failures (identified by operations or maintenance), facilities and equipment upgrades, safety or environmental concerns, preventive maintenance (PMs) that are due, customer requests or aesthetic improvements etc. It is expected that the work requester indicate verbally or in writing what is required (describing the asset, the problem, the account to charge), an attempt at diagnosing the problem, how important the request is and how soon it should be addressed. Usually the requester files a copy of the request before sending it off to the party responsible for addressing the re-

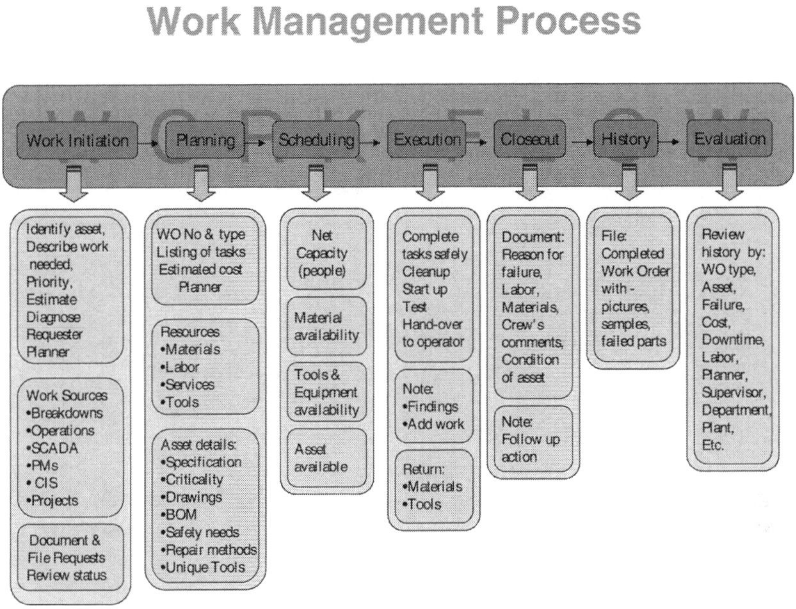

Work Management Process

Work Initiation	Planning	Scheduling	Execution	Closeout	History	Evaluation
Identify asset, Describe work needed, Priority, Estimate Diagnose Requester Planner	WO No & type Listing of tasks Estimated cost Planner	Net Capacity (people)	Complete tasks safely Cleanup Start up Test Hand-over to operator	Document: Reason for failure, Labor, Materials, Crew's comments, Condition of asset	File: Completed Work Order with - pictures, samples, failed parts	Review history by: WO type, Asset, Failure, Cost, Downtime, Labor, Planner, Supervisor, Department, Plant, Etc.
Work Sources •Breakdowns •Operations •SCADA •PMs • CIS •Projects	Resources •Materials •Labor •Services •Tools	Material availability	Note: •Findings •Add work	Note: Follow up action		
Document & File Requests Review status	Asset details: •Specification •Criticality •Drawings •BOM •Safety needs •Repair methods •Unique Tools	Tools & Equipment availability Asset available	Return: •Materials •Tools			

FIGURE 6.13 *Work flow in the Work Management Process.*

quest. The initiator will regularly monitor the status of this request (sometimes identified by a number), depending on the importance of the work order task.

Work Planning

The request created by the initiator eventually finds its way to the person who is responsible for planning the work order task. Workflow parameters dictate how quickly the request reaches its final destination and how quickly it receives action. At this stage, the planner can either plan the work order task from scratch or as is usually the case in most industries use a previous work order task as a template. This is the stage where the work request becomes a work order. The planner needs the details on the asset to be worked on (criticality, specifications, safety/environmental (permit) requirements etc.), work methods applicable to the asset, spares and services typically used in repairs. The detailed tasks, based on the work methods, can then be developed with the appropriate labor, material (materials, tools and special equipment) and services needed to execute the task. At this stage the planner has a good estimate of how much the entire work order task will cost and can seek an approval to proceed using workflow. Once approved, the work order becomes active and joins the other work orders in the work order backlog. At the same time, all materials are ordered through stores check out requests (or material requisitions) for items stocked in the stores. Any non-stores or services items are ordered through the purchasing system. Workflow plays an important role at this phase in order to meet policy guidelines on spending limitations.

Work Scheduling

Scheduling of work orders is the process of identifying which work order tasks will be done, when they will be done, and by which crew and/or employees. A work order can be scheduled to be done on a specific day and time with a hundred percent (100%) surety only if all scheduling elements are in place. For this phase to be effective it is important that all materials, services, tools, special equipment, labor (commonly referred to as net capacity) are available together with the asset, for work to be done on it. If any of these scheduling elements are not in place, the work order or task cannot be done, and there will be consequential non-value-added time associated with waiting while efforts are made to resolve the problem. Workflow is the framework that ensures all elements are in place before a work order is scheduled. The result of scheduling efforts is a list or lists of work order tasks (with relevant details such as tasks, permits and drawings) that will be done by crews or individuals on a specific day, week, or month.

Work Execution

Once a work order is scheduled, workers can proceed with the execution phase by collecting materials, tools and equipment, arranging "lock out and tag out" or other permitting requirements and proceed with the various tasks. During the actual work, there must be access to information that was not provided (e.g., assembly drawings, clearances, torque values etc.) or different spares, add or modify the tasks based on new information that become available. Tasks may be completed in a matter of hours or may continue for days and weeks. Noting work progress, completion and the crew's observations, findings during the repair or overhaul process is an important aspect of the execution phase. This information is a vital step in optimizing the planning process for future work on the asset. Completion of the job should trigger certain workflow activities such as informing the requester that the job is completed.

Work Closeout

This is a component of the work management process that has been lacking in most industries. Generally, the focus is on doing the work as quickly as possible, so as to be able to move on to another job. Any completion details, crew's comments etc. are either not recorded or are limited to employee time charged to the work order. This is the component of the work management process that enables the optimization of work by providing an opportunity to capture valuable work history in addition to task detail and cost. Reasons for failure, follow-on work, descriptive details on failed components, photographs, videos etc. are some of the ways to capture what happened.

Work History

All the data/information created directly or indirectly from the preceding components of the work management process provide history for use in the evaluation phase. Generally this information is stored as files that can be paper or electronic. The index system is usually based on the asset number by plant or facility or the responsible supervisor. Ideally, all relevant information is regularly added to the files to build the history of what work is done on the asset. It is important that the appropriate data be added and also that there be quality control of the actual data provided.

Work Evaluation

The work evaluation component of the work management process is essential to provide feedback for the planning and scheduling components. On a day-to-day basis, the planner needs to know if the right job plan was put together with accurate determinations of resources and time to do the actual task. If there is any variance, the planner should be able to improve the accuracy of the planning function. Similarly, feedback on the actual findings from work done (close out data) may dictate a change in the preventive maintenance frequencies for PM tasks. Data from predictive type tasks would be useful in programming subsequent follow up corrective work. Where a corrective work order was executed, close out data can be useful in evaluation of the accuracy of the predictions from condition monitoring tasks. Finally, it is always a good practice when planning and scheduling work, to check on previous work done to identify failure trends and program-upgrade or improvement-type work orders, instead of repeating the same repair work as in the past.

Program-Driven Work

Program-driven work is the business process that allows you to take control of the work management process and ensure that the right work is done at the right time on the right assets. When work is done poorly you can find yourself in a reactive work environment, where you have little or no control on what is happening and all efforts are focused on getting assets back into production at any cost. On the other hand, you can find yourself doing too much proactive work where the focus is on efficiency—everything seems to be under control but a lot of work is being done at a high cost. The ideal situation is *Optimized Work* where the focus is on effectiveness—the right work is done at the right time on the right assets. Figure 6.14 shows the transition to the Optimized Work environment.

Reactive Work

In reactive work there is little or no planning and scheduling of work.

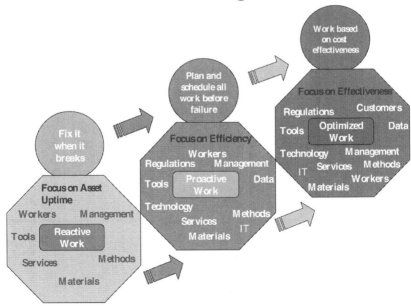

FIGURE 6.14 *The Journey to an Optimized Work Environment.*

The prevailing atmosphere is often one of frustration, as employees repair assets or perform a work order task on an ad hoc basis, due to revenue loss or safety concerns. In a reactive work environment, reactive work can be over 75% with only 25%% of the total wok being planned. There is a high cost associated with work execution that includes high labor (overtime), materials, services, and opportunity due to equipment downtime. In addition, there can be high costs associated with secondary damage to equipment as a result of catastrophic failure. In a reactive operation, assets are unreliable and the maintenance philosophy is "fix it when it breaks." There is obsolete equipment being maintained, lack of appropriate spares, and poor service from the stores and purchasing support group. Little effort is made to standardize equipment, parts, equipment, and performance levels.

Proactive Work

In the proactive work situation, there is control on the workload through good execution of the work management process. Proactive work is fully supported by other processes such as Inventory, Purchasing and Accounts Payables. There is good planning and scheduling with detailed work plans and all supporting resources available for work execution. It is not uncommon to find the percentage of planned work close to 100% of all the work being done in this type of operation. There is, however, little focus on cost-effectiveness, and equipment reliability is sometimes achieved at a high cost (materials, labor, services and the opportunity cost associated with equipment downtime during repairs or overhaul). There is improved reliability through extensive planning and scheduling of work. Preventive maintenance work order tasks are in place for all assets and components regardless of the criticality. As a result, equipment is usually shut down, serviced, overhauled or lubricated when there really is no indication of a problem. Reliability of equipment increases but at a premium cost. There is a high cost of labor, materials and services associated with the work management process. In addition, there is the opportunity cost associated with reduced process rate when equipment is out of service. This is sometime overcome by using extensive overtime on the "off shift" hours to meet the preventive maintenance schedule.

Optimized Work

In an optimized work environment there is an appropriate mix of planned and reactive work based on cost effectiveness. The optimum split is 75% proactive work and 25% reactive work (Figure 6.15) in general (this split can vary by ±(5–10%) based on the type of industry). The split is achieved through the identification of critical equipment, selection of the appropriate repair tactics using Reliability Centered Maintenance, predicting potential failures using predictive maintenance, and condition-monitoring techniques and the use of data for decision making. The underlying culture is one of continuous improvement, and this is achieved through a team-based empowered organization working under Total Productive Maintenance concepts. Reliability Centered Maintenance (RCM) and Predictive Maintenance (PdM) are used in conjunction with preventive maintenance to do appropriate work on assets with a goal of extending the mean time between failure (MTBF) or reliability of assets. Data collected in the course of doing work using the CWMS is routinely used to evaluate and modify the work planned for assets. Cost effective reliability is usually achieved to satisfy the needs of the user, safety and environmental regulations.

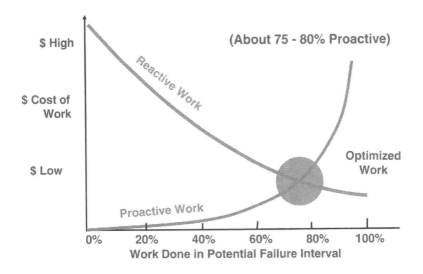

FIGURE 6.15 *Optimized Work.*

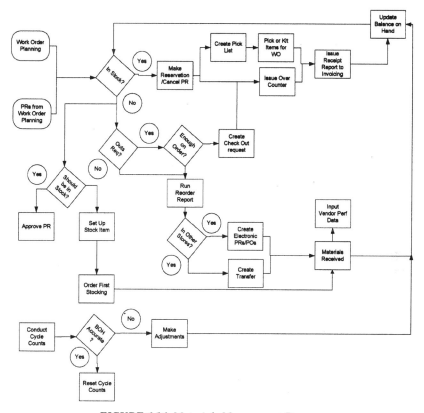

FIGURE 6.16 *Materials Management Process.*

Materials Management (in support of the work order planning process)

Having the right materials and services available on time and of the proper quality and specifications is the ultimate goal for materials management in the support of work management. This can be achieved by the right balance of onsite stocking or timely purchase from suitable vendors. This would require automatic reservations of stock items and the creation of pick lists for items to be staged for the work order at the stores, or electronic requisitions to buyers for the goods and services to be purchased from vendors. Figure 6.16 provides an overview of the business process for effective MRO materials management. This process is best done using a CWMS, where the work order management, inventory and purchasing functionality are core modules of the system. The

CWMS functionality should provide seamless access to each of these modules from the work order module during the planning phase for WOs.

When materials management is done effectively the following results are observed:

- High service level with a desired target of 98% (i.e., 98% of the time, when employees visit the stores for materials to support work management they get what they want)
- Right mix of centralized and decentralized stores
- Stock levels are based on economic order and safety stock level quantities
- Proactive materials management is practiced—use of pick lists and kitting of parts for work orders
- Bar coding and mobile devices are employed to expedite the various stores transactions
- Right mix of just in time, consignment and traditional stocking practices are employed

Predictive Maintenance (PdM)

All assets deteriorate with use; in fact some assets deteriorate even if they are not being operated due to environmental impact etc. Most assets have a predictable deterioration curve (Figure 6.17), and understanding this concept can help you maximize the use of the asset before you have to take it out of service. There are three major points on the curve that are of interest:

(1) Where failure starts to occur but is not possible to detect the failure rate using available techniques.

(2) Point at which failure is detectable using available techniques.

(3) Point at which the asset is unable to meet the performance standards from its users—essentially the asset has experienced a functional failure.

Figure 6.16. Predictive Maintenance (PdM) techniques help track the condition of the asset in the potential failure zone and provide data on its condition. Some practitioners refer to this as Condition Based Monitoring (CBM). The goal is for the maintenance staff to intervene just before the failure point and bring the asset condition back to 100%. Many different predictive techniques are applicable to different categories of assets. Appendix 6.2 provides an overview of the various available techniques by asset type. Obviously it is not cost effective to carry out predictive

Asset Deterioration Curve

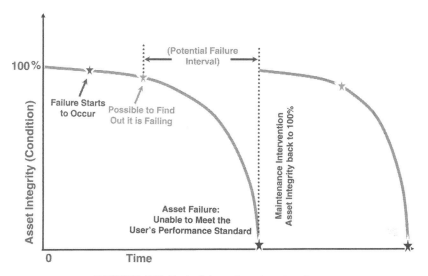

FIGURE 6.17 *Typical Asset Deterioration Curve.*

maintenance on every asset. Also, it is not cost effective to train up internal staff to do all predictive techniques in-house. It is important to understand the necessary components of a PdM program and how it ties into the other maintenance processes. Figure 6.18 shows the key elements of a PdM program:

- *Step 1*—determine critical equipment for inclusion in the program. Candidates for the program should be based on asset criticality, replacement cost, impact on the operations, environment and safety as a result of failure.
- *Step 2*—determine the predictive techniques that are applicable to the particular asset category and specific asset. (e.g., vibration analysis for monitoring bearing assemblies). This step needs to include the process for determining if the service will be developed internally or will be provided by partnership with external service providers. Some criteria to consider in this decision process would be: amount of work, cost of instruments and tools, costs to keep staff skilled and competent in doing monitoring and evaluation, ability to build a knowledge base for identifying potential failures before they occur.

- *Step 3*—create the Preventive Maintenance (PM) tasks in the CWMS for measurement based on appropriate frequencies. Develop resource and task detail (e.g., type of instrument, skill set).
- *Step 4*—carry out the PdM task, measure, trend the data. In other words construct the deterioration curve for the asset.
- *Step 5*—identify when the asset is close to the functional failure point and create a work request to carry out the relevant maintenance intervention (could be a component change out or a complete overhaul).
- *Step 6*—optimize the PdM program, evaluate the effectiveness of the program update frequencies for measurement and the need for additional PdM techniques.

Deliverables from a PdM program

- Predictive PMs for various assets
- Condition-monitoring data and associated failure curves for various critical assets

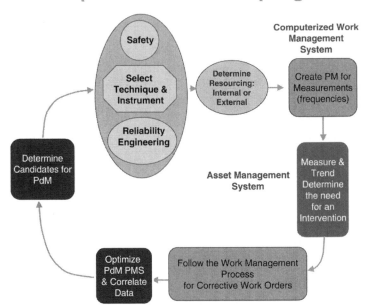

FIGURE 6.18 *Predictive Maintenance Supports Asset Management.*

- Completed corrective work orders for all problems identified prior to actual failure
- Partnerships with suppliers of PdM services not provided in house
- Benefits tracking for the program

Reliability Centered Maintenance (RCM)

How do you determine the maintenance tasks for assets—fix it when it breaks, do time-based PMs, predictive maintenance? Typically we depend on: trial and error, the guidelines from the manufacturer, the experience gained by senior practitioners over the years in the business, or through Reliability Centered Maintenance[6] (RCM). The latter is a structured process that allows you to determine the right maintenance tactic for the asset in its operating context. This technique was pioneered in the military by Nowlan and Heap many years ago and has been adopted as a standard business process in the aircraft industry to ensure reliability. Many other industries have experimented with RCM and have found value from the process. RCM is now finding its way into many industries as a necessary and important technique for setting up the maintenance program. The RCM process is shown in Figure 6.18.

When and asset is selected for an RCM analysis, it's important that the operating context of the asset is fully understood. The following questions take you through the RCM process:

(1) What are the functions and associated performance standards of the assets in its present operating context?
(2) What constitutes a failure—in what ways does it fail to fulfill its functions?
(3) What causes each functional failure?
(4) What happens when each failure occurs, how does each failure matter?
(5) What can we do about it: what can be done to predict or prevent each failure, what should be done if a suitable proactive task cannot be found?

Answers to the above questions will systematically take you to the goal of developing failure- management plans (*deliverables from an*

[6]Reliability Centered Maintenance II, Second Edition by John Moubrey published by Industrial Press, 1997.

Reliability Engineering:
Doing the Right Tasks at the Right Time

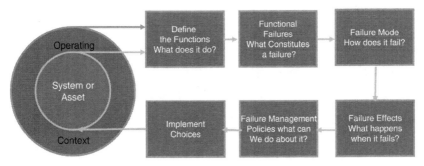

FIGURE 6.19 RCM process.

RCM process) for your assets. These can be a mixture of proactive and reactive tasks addressing the failed state of the asset:

- *Proactive tasks*—undertaken before a failure occurs, in order to prevent the item from getting into a failed state (predictive, preventive tasks).
- *Default actions*—deal with the failed state and chosen when it is not possible to identify an effective proactive task (failure-finding, redesign, run-to-failure).

The benefits of RCM are—greater safety and environmental integrity, improved operating performance, greater maintenance cost effectiveness, longer useful life of expensive equipment, comprehensive database on assets and maintenance requirements and better motivation and teamwork.

Operations Management

Operations management is a broad topic, and its content varies based on the industry, product, and service being produced. Figure 6.19 shows the key concepts in operations management:

There are, however, key concepts that must be considered if you want to excel in operating your assets to create a quality good or service and keep your customers satisfied at all times:

- *Unattended or less attended operations*—the drive to reduce labor costs and increase productivity through automation is pushing the envelope in automated designs for processes. Smart systems are able to conduct self diagnosis and alert the operator to quality issues, asset heath problems and fail in a safe mode, when operating conditions are not safe for the asset. On the global front, automation is the only way for first-world countries to be able to compete with the cheaper labor rates from third-world countries. The downsides to automation are the additional complexity and associated maintenance requirements for the automation components and loss of jobs.

- *Production planning*—production planning can be a simple concept if you are creating one product continuously. In real life, however, companies make and market many different products and services using the same assets. The process of planning the production runs, materials requirements, changeovers and logistics to meet different customer demands is referred to as production planning. This can be very complicated and if done poorly can lead to major cost inefficiency. Fortunately, there is good business software to help with this process, as well as professional production planners.
- *Statistical process control*—SPC tracks processes. Again, there is process control or SCADA software that can track various process

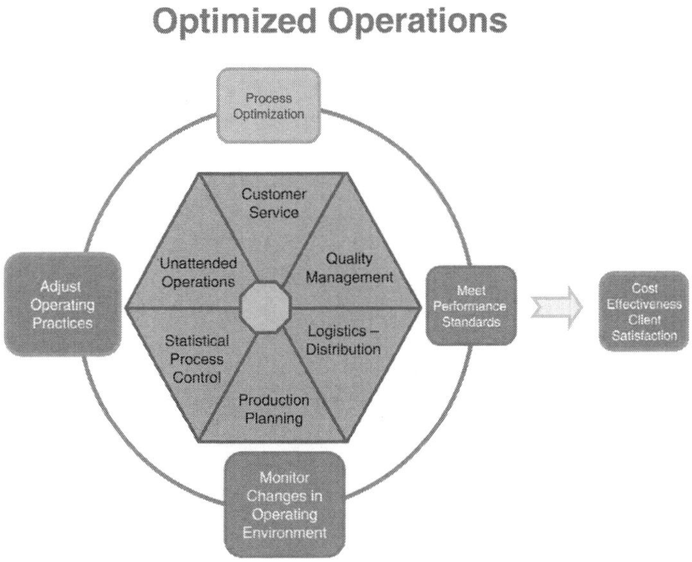

Optimized Operations

FIGURE 6.20 *Optimized Operations.*

elements with alarm- and fault-ranges and allow operators to see graphically when different process components or the overall process is deviating from desired norms. Statistical process control helps ensure quality standards in products and services.

- *Quality management*—quality and customer service go hand in hand. Obviously, a poor product or poor service will lead to customer dissatisfaction. This is further exacerbated if the customer is paying a premium for the product or service. A good quality assurance program (framework for assuring high quality) and good quality control (actual execution of the program) will reduce losses from rejects, work in progress, and also dissatisfied customers. Quality applies to services, as well as products. In both cases the company must be clear on what is acceptable and manage to these targets.

- *Logistics*—doing a great job in all areas is commendable but the job is not done until the product or service reaches the hands of the end user or customer. Ensuring that your warehousing, management of middle men, transportation and distribution of the product is done effectively is important in keeping costs and losses down, keeping customers highly satisfied and sustaining a high-performance organization.

- *Customer service*—successful companies have learnt the hard lesson that the customer is king. They excel at customer service, leveraging technology assets to manage call centers, utilizing queuing theories to minimize waiting time, training of service representatives and gaining important feedback for the people who use their product or service on how to make improvements. Many companies are leveraging technology in the form of *Customer Resource Management Systems* to capture and use important data about customer service and customer preferences. This is a critical element in operations management. It remains true that it is much harder to generate a new customer than keep an existing one!

By understanding the requirements for each of these areas and practicing them, you can be assured of optimized operations—being effective at creating and getting the most from assets in products or services and at the same time keeping the customer satisfied.

Total Productive Maintenance (TPM)

Total Productive Maintenance is a set of ideas, practices and tools that have evolved from initial work by Japanese engineer, Seichi Nakajima.

After studying American preventive maintenance practices, he formulated an approach called Total Productive Maintenance (TPM). This approach was first implemented during the 1970s at Toyota. Its implementation adapted the ideas of Just-In-Time manufacturing to maintenance, and it dramatically increased equipment reliability. Nakajima recognized that there are three major loss categories:

- *Availability Losses*—the equipment is not available to produce output.
- *Performance Losses*—the equipment is operating below standard.
- *Quality Losses*—the equipment is producing defective output.

Figure 6.21, provides an overview of the focus areas for TPM and the recommended implementation approach.

(1) *Autonomous Maintenance*—operators take an active role in the basic care of the asset. They perform Cleaning, Lubrication, Adjustments, Inspections and Repairs (commonly knowing CLAIR).

(2) *Asset Improvement*—The objective of equipment improvement is to reduce losses that occur due to a lack of equipment reliability. Equipment improvement consists of identifying the losses that

Total Productive Maintenance

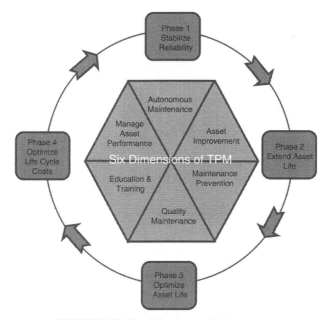

FIGURE 6.21 *Total Productive Maintenance.*

have the greatest impact on the utility and attack them in an organized way to reduce / control or eliminate the problems at the root. Equipment improvement is a process of continuous improvement that never stops trying to create gains in efficiency and effectiveness. Equipment improvement focuses on both the operation and the maintenance of equipment.

(3) *Maintenance Prevention*—The goal of maintenance prevention is to reduce or eliminate all unnecessary maintenance activity. This is achieved by both avoiding potential problems and solving existing problems.

(4) *Quality Maintenance*—The objective of quality maintenance is to operate a plant with 100% defect-free equipment that produces defect-free products. While this goal can never be fully achieved, it does provide the ultimate goal to strive towards. In order to approach this objective, the following actions must take place: identify the equipment conditions necessary to produce zero defects, check and measure these conditions on a scheduled basis to ensure they are within specifications, and prepare and analyze trends and take corrective action to prevent unacceptable variations.

(5) *Education and Training*—The objective of education and training is to ensure that all TPM team members develop the skills and knowledge required to become effective TPM team members. Education and training focus on building the work and communication skills required for the work environment..

(6) *Manage Asset Performance*—Understanding what the user wants from the asset and managing all operations and maintenance activities to meet the performance target are necessary for asset performance. It is therefore recommended to develop Key Performance metrics (KPIs) with associated targets.

Phased Approach to Implementation

A phased approach to TPM implementation is highly recommended because:

- It is more economical to lengthen equipment life by eliminating accelerated deterioration.
- Until accelerated deterioration is arrested, true design weaknesses usually are invisible.
- Even if weaknesses are corrected, the overall effect may be masked by accelerated deterioration.

- Application of systematic maintenance is most effective in a stable, predictable environment.

The recommended approach has four major phases:

- Phase I—Stabilize Reliability
- Phase II—Lengthen Asset Life
- Phase III—Optimize Asset Life
- Phase IV—Optimize Lifecycle Cost

Results from a TPM Program

- Maintenance staff benefits include:
  —Higher level of expertise through training and enhanced job experience
  —More time for preventive, predictive, and diagnostic maintenance
  —Less time spent on routine lubrication, adjustments, cleaning and inspections
  —Improved coordination between operations and maintenance
  —Higher proficiency in more craft areas through multi-skilling
- Operation staff benefits include:
  —Better equipment reliability and availability
  —Increased control over equipment and process decisions
  —Greater expertise via training and experience
  —Improved communications and relationships with maintenance staff
  —Greater job satisfaction by doing more meaningful work and by allowing staff to use more skills and abilities
- The organization benefits include:
  —Longer equipment life and lower lifecycle costs
  —More uptime by having fewer breakdowns
  —More throughput and higher product quality
  —Higher employee productivity due to greater job satisfaction
  —Lower staff turnover due to employee satisfaction

Six-Sigma (6σ)

Six sigma is defined as a highly technical method used by engineers and statisticians to reduce defects in processes. Six-sigma has been viewed as pursuing a goal of near-perfection in meeting customer requirements by achieving 3.4 parts per million potential defects. Cultural change can also be achieved in the pursuit of six-sigma. In summary, six sigma is a methodology that provides businesses with the tools to improve the capability of their business processes. The increase in performance and decrease in process variation lead to defect reduction and improvement in profits, employee morale, and product quality.

Lean Manufacturing

The relentless elimination of waste is the main concept behind the just-in-time or lean production system. Lean thinking or its principles can be applied in the service industry as well as in manufacturing industries to reduce lead time, improve quality and productivity by eliminating wastes in the system. Effective industrial engineering practice is needed to eliminate waste. At least 95% of cycle time in a non-lean factory or office consists of non-value-added activities. Lean manufacturing and CI thinking go hand-in-hand. Lean manufacturing can reduce waste in the following areas:

- Over production ahead of demand.
- Waiting for the next process step of information.
- Transporting materials unnecessarily.
- Over-processing and non-value added processing.
- Inventory that is more than bare minimum.
- Motion by employees that is unnecessary.
- Producing non-conforming parts.

Upgrade/Modify/Replace:

The essential business process that needs to be discussed upgrading is how O&M staff determines when it is necessary to upgrade, modify or replace an existing asset. When this decision is clear, then how do O&M justify the investment needed to execute the decision? Upgrade and modify type decisions are usually driven by capacity increases, need to be more energy and environmentally friendly (meet stricter regulations), and/or safety. Asset replacement decisions are usually a lot more difficult. Often, there may be very little cost and work history data on the asset and the current asset condition. The situation can be further exacerbated when the data cannot be trusted. However, with some effort it is usually possible to go back through history records, previous budgets etc. and pull together enough data to build a business case for asset replacement. Figure 6.22 shows the four steps in the business case process:

Business Case and Benefits Tracking Steps

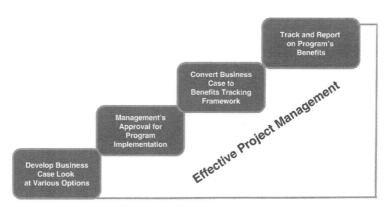

FIGURE 6.22 *Business Case Process.*

- *Step 1*—develop the business case (look at various alternatives)—Figure 6.23 and Figure 6.24 are examples of the output from an economic analysis for major asset replacement project.
- *Step 2*—seek approval from management for the program (should be straightforward if a good job is done at step 1).
- *Step 3*—convert the business case to a benefits tracking document to be used during project execution.

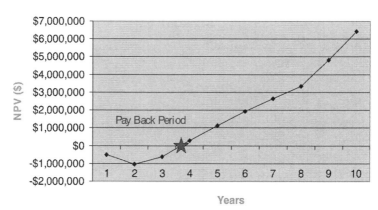

FIGURE 6.23 *Economic Analysis for a Major Asset Replacement.*

Business Case: Scenarios Show that it is Economically Feasible to Replace the Asset

Business Case Scenario	NPV	IRR	Payback Period	Comment
Alternative, Design 1	$ 9M	16%	6 yrs	Not attractive
Alternative, Design 2	$ 10M	42%	4 yrs	Good project option
Alternative, Design 3	$ 15M	55%	3 yrs	Best Alternative
Alternative, Keep Asset	$ 3M	3%	n/a	Not attractive
Notes: Project life is 10yrs				
WACC is 15%				

FIGURE 6.24 *Economic Analysis for Major Asset Replacement Project.*

- *Step 4*—track and report on the benefits from the project; this is essential to gain the confidence of management.

Decommission or Take Out of Service

While at first it seems there is not value in it, decommissioning is very important to the asset lifecycle. Sometimes, it is necessary to decommission and "mothball" certain assets because it is uneconomical to operate the asset as a result of market trends (reduced demand or low and uncompetitive product prices). Many times, the asset is no longer useful and has to be permanently taken out of service usually because of technological obsolescence or no more demand for the product or service. In both cases there are certain practices you must consider:

- *Decommission or mothball:*
  - —Protection from deterioration due to the weather
  - —Internal corrosion or breakdown of process products—it is necessary to displace all of the process products with an inert substance that protects against degradation or corrosion
  - —Lubricate all valves, shafts, bearings and seals
  - —Protection against accidental start up—disconnect all service lines, utilities (gas and electricity)
  - —Security—protection for people who may inadvertently access the site or deliberately access the site to pilfer or sabotage
  - —Secure all asset documentation—specifications, drawings, bill of materials, manuals of practices, cost and work history

   —Secure all operating and MRO spares
   —Develop documentation on re-commissioning procedures
- *Permanent removal:*
   —Maximize the revenue from salvage value of the asset or asset components—usually in the form of scrap metal or resale of components to other companies who still operate the asset
   —Follow environmental regulations for restoring site to original condition
   —Proper disposal of toxic or hazardous materials
   — Documentation of any underground assets that will remain after site restoration

The above are the major business process associated with the typical asset lifecycle. The suggested approach for realizing a vision of sustainable asset management must be considered in your own operating context and business environment. This is most obvious with the globalization of most industries. Business processes in first-world and third-world countries will vary based on the unique requirements of these countries. For example, cheaper labor rates, less stringent environmental regulations and corporate taxes may influence asset design and O&M practices.

APPENDIX 6.1—SAMPLE VISION AND MISSION STATEMENTS FOR ASSET MANAGEMENT (PUBLIC WORKS OPERATIONS)

Vision

Our vision for sustainable asset management is to create, operate and maintain assets at the lowest overall cost of ownership, so that they meet public heath and safety needs of our citizens today while at the same time considering the needs of the future generation.

Mission

We will fulfill the vision by ensuring that:

- Groups responsible for planning, financing, designing, purchasing, constructing, operating and maintaining the assets will have an active role in the decision-making process.

- Performance standards will be designed and managed to meet customer expectations, regulations and employee safety.
- New assets will only be introduced in to the mix after careful supply- and demand-side analysis.
- Asset creation, replacement, and disposal decisions will be based on sound economic criteria.

APPENDIX 6.2—LISTING OF PREDICTIVE TECHNIQUES

Predictive or condition-based monitoring techniques are essentially classified by the type of symptom or potential failure that they monitor. They can be dynamic, particle, chemical, physical, temperature and electrical effects. The choice of an appropriate technique should be based on the asset, its operating context and cost considerations. RCM analysis provides a robust method for determining the appropriate monitoring technique and frequency. The following is a partial listing of some of the techniques available in given areas (you can get more information from the book Reliability Centered Maintenance II by John Moubray[3] or any of the standard texts on predictive or condition-based maintenance):

1.0 Dynamic Monitoring
    1.1 Vibration analysis
    1.2 Ultrasonic analysis
    1.3 Acoustic emissions
2.0 Particle
    2.1 Ferrography
    2.2 Particle counter
    2.3 Chip detection (magnetic)
    2.4 Sediment test
    2.5 Oil analysis
3.0 Chemical
    3.1 Oil analysis
    3.2 Atomic emission spectroscopy
    3.3 Infrared spectroscopy
    3.4 Gas chromatography
    3.5 Scanning electron microscope
    3.6 Electro-chemical corrosion monitoring
4.0 Physical
    4.1 Liquid dye penetrants

CHAPTER 7

Organization Design and People Effectiveness

DEVELOPING A HIGH-PERFORMANCE ORGANIZATION TO SUPPORT ASSET MANAGEMENT

People effectiveness is one of the three essential components for becoming effective at asset management. The strategies recommended for developing a high-performance organization to support asset management were discussed briefly in Chapter 6:

- organizational and people effectiveness
- corporate knowledge retention
- performance management

We will now explain these strategies in detail and define their relationship to asset management.

Organizational and People Effectiveness

A company's vision and mission statement will identify the business they are in and will set the stage for the assets necessary to create the service or product for the client base. The combination of assets into various processes and systems will determine the business processes that the organization must excel at to be competitive and a best in class organization. Figure 7.1 shows the steps involved in developing and sustaining a high-performance organization needed to support effective asset management (this process can be applied to existing organizations or building a new organization).

Organizational Effectiveness

FIGURE 7.1 *Developing a High-performance Organization.*

Step 1—Define or Validate Asset and Business Process Requirements Necessary to Achieve the Company's Vision and Mission

In order to develop the basic framework for the way people interact with assets, a number of areas must be clearly understood and documented.

- *Number and types of assets to be used in production of the good or service*—this will dictate the skill level required.
- *Working environment*—harsh working conditions, e.g., offshore oil and gas operations and mining will require different skill sets compared to an operations in a factory where there are less hazards.
- *Level of automation*—will dictate the complexity of the various processes and also determine the needed skill level for operations and maintenance.
- *Type of asset ownership:*
  —Full ownership will require more investment in people resources.

—Leased assets will require operational staff (if maintenance is carried out by asset owner).

—Assets owned by company but operated and maintained by a contractor—this may eliminate the need for O&M staff but will increase the need for contract management resources.

These factors dictate the type of business processes that will be undertaken by the organization in order to be successful at executing its vision and mission. Each business process must be carefully mapped out, in terms of the steps required to achieve its output or hand off to another group. The workflow must be fully documented together with the roles, responsibilities, skills, non-productive assets (technology, tools and equipment) requirements, and performance measures. This information will be a key input into the organization design and subsequent phases.

Step 2—Develop the Organization Structure Needed to Execute the Business Processes on the Asset Mix to Deliver the Service or Create the Product to the Customer Base

The structural configuration of a company (or organizational design) is the way work is divided and how it achieves coordination among its various work activities. In our context, work activities around the asset lifecycle. A company's structure resolves the two basic tasks of getting work done by:

- Dividing up the work in the organization.
- Ensuring the work gets done by providing the coordination and control of work.

Understanding the assets and the work needed to create, operate, and maintain these assets to create a product or service is fundamental to the organizational design process. Organization design is the series of management decisions needed to achieve the company's vision and mission that gets translated into the strategies and tactics in the strategic plan. Figure 7.2 shows that there are four major organizational arrangements that can be interpreted for a company's unique business environment:

(1) Division of labor.
(2) Allocation of authority.
(3) Departmentalization.
(4) Span of control.

Organization Design Principles:

FIGURE 7.2 *Organization Design Principles.*

It is therefore conceivable that you can have an organization design that on one extreme is very mechanistic where there is high division of labor, low delegation of authority, departments with high uniformity of work and narrow span of controls. Such organizations exhibit a culture of tight rules and policies, limited individual job discretion, and coordination which is formal and written. Similarly, it is possible to have an organic design where there is low division of labor, a high level of delegation, departments with low uniformity of work and large spans of control. Such organizations exhibit a culture where there are few rules and procedures to follow, people expect face-to-face or informal coordination and expect to be empowered to create their own work plans and schedules. There could be organization designs that fit anywhere in between these two extremes. Clearly, management needs to decide on the configuration up front on what design will allow its people resources to be effective at coordinating and executing all work around the asset lifecycle.

Some of the more popular organization designs that have been successful are:

Functional design—Functional design is a logical reflection of the company's activities. It is based on specialization that is efficient (e.g., the engineering department provides planning and design services). Individuals learn to speak a common language (maintenance, operations, purchasing, stores etc.). It minimizes duplication of effort. Training of employees is focused and simplified. There is tight organizational control and the legitimate authority of the chain of command is reinforced. This may work well in many situations; however, there are some inherent issues that management must be wary of: overspecialization and narrowing of business viewpoints in the departments, development of managers limited to their functional areas (limited cross-training), weak coordination across departments, tendency to create empires. The person at the top of the organization can become overloaded, and managers tend to lose sight of the reason they are in business: to be very profitable at keeping customers delighted. A sample organization design is given in Appendix 7.1.

Product design—product design provides for adaptability and flexibility in meeting the needs of managers as they use assets to create a set of related products. Some strong points of this design are: external changes relevant to the customer and products can be detected more readily, employees gain a deep understanding of products and customer needs, friendly competition can arise among business units, performance management is easy to implement and manage and the design allows for a shifting in responsibility from the CEO to the business unit manager. As with the other designs, there are challenges that managers must be aware off and must deal with effectively: duplication of effort and resources, difficulty recruitment managers who have all the skills and expertise to be effective, conflicts that arise from sharing resources and agreeing on "transfer prices."

Territorial design—territorial design establishes work groups based on a geographic area. One manager can control all work activities in a single region. Work can be customized to the unique requirements of customers in the region (e.g. North America and Europe). Managers can develop a broad skill set, good training for career development. Business units are very responsive to the customer's needs. There are also inherent issues with this design that management must be aware of: duplication of effort and unused excess asset capacity or resources. Also, it may be difficult to find managers who are effective in all business functions.

Matrix design—the matrix design is composed of project managers and project teams who are employees from functional business units. There is a need for a project manager and the team remains intact for the duration of the project. Teams can have multiple bosses, one or more project managers and/or a functional boss. Advantages to this design are: combined strength of functional and product designs, better departmental coordination, project teams can easily focus on its goals and objectives and the organization can create temporary teams to focus on specific projects without creating permanent business units. The disadvantages include: confusing to employees, seems to violate the "unity of command" principle, requires excellent planning and resource allocation, project managers must have excellent technical, political and communication skills, and the design can lead to excessive overhead costs as each team hires technical and support staff. A sample design is given in Appendix 7.1.

Step 3—Define Roles, Responsibilities, Performance Standards, Skills and Competencies, Job Description and Staffing Numbers

The decisions made in Steps 1 and 2 above will set the stage for determining the roles, responsibilities, and skill levels needed to coordinate and execute the work in the company. It is now necessary to combine these into jobs that will be done by each individual in the company i.e. from CEO to the operator or maintainer. The next big question that must be answered is how many individuals are needed for each job. This is a difficult task. If it is not done properly, you can end up with too many staff and obvious inefficiencies. Similarly, too little staff will result in issues that limit your ability to realize the full potential from your assets. There are many ways to determine initial staffing numbers, e.g., time and motion studies, resource loading, comparison to similar industries and businesses. Optimal staffing numbers also depend on having effective business processes enabled by the integrated technology asset solution. For an existing business, it is necessary to work backwards to determine the optimal staffing necessary to get the most from the assets. This means redesigning business processes so that they are based on best practices, eliminating all non-value added steps, and maximizing technology. In addition, a review of the organization design may also lead to efficiencies through ending duplication of resources, better delegating, empowering of staff, multi-skilling and workforce flexibility. It is essential in this step that you strive to achieve the optimal staffing numbers necessary to effectively manage all of your assets around the various business processes in the respective asset lifecycles.

Step 4—Develop and Implement Underlying Organizational Concepts Necessary to Nurture and Keep the Organization Operating Smoothly

- *Human resources principles*—HR should set the stage for how the company and its staff interact. It should define the company's standards in terms of ethics, equal employment opportunity, sexual harassment and the employee's rights. These principles will also help define the level of attractiveness of the company to prospective employees.

- *A collective agreement with your union partner*—In companies where there is one or more unions representing the interest of staff, the collective agreement formalizes how the company and union will partner in ensuring that management and employees work. together. The agreement formalizes the different types of jobs, compensation, benefits, disciplinary action and the grievance process. Many union management relationships tend to be adversarial, and the collective agreement is used to gain advantage. Companies should strive for participative management with unions, where the relation is more of a partnership focused on creating and sustaining a high-performance and competitive organization where everyone wins.
- *Compensation and benefit plans*—Compensation is often driven by negotiations with a union. Ideally, such negotiations occur within a mutually participative agreement procedure.
- *Career development and performance appraisals*—Many companies pay lip service to career development. In fact, when performance appraisal time comes, it is usually a surprise for most managers and a pain to complete all appraisals to meet the set deadlines. Many employees being reviewed are surprised to find out about weaknesses that no one told them about during the entire year. Instead of a pleasant meeting where and employee and her manager can work together and plan for the employee's career, these sessions can break down into controversies. Individual performance management is an ongoing process and the end-of-year performance appraisal should be an opportunity to formalize the expectations (hopefully aligned by now both positive and negative) of both the manager and employee. In the scenario where an employee has been doing well and has responded to coaching and mentoring, the appraisal process is the opportunity for the manager to meet the expectations that have been set. In the event that an employee has not been meeting the manager's expectations and has not responded well to coaching and mentoring, then making a decision to part ways will be beneficial to both the company and the employee who may very well be the wrong fit for the organization. This decision may also help the employee. Career development and performance appraisal are closely aligned with a company's retention strategy.

Retention entails attention to the following:

- *Recruitment*—Hiring the right people is possibly the best start you can have. This is obviously a moot point when you have an existing workforce, a strong and militant union, and few opportunities for new hires! However, for new organizations, or those experiencing growth, here are recruiting concepts that should be kept in mind:

(1) Develop a general profile of the type of people that will fit your organization and enjoy working in the organization as they achieve their goals and objectives.

(2) Develop detailed job descriptions clearly defining roles, responsibilities, qualifications, experience, skills and associated competencies.

(3) Develop a compensation and benefits package to attract the type of people you want to hire.

(4) Find the right pool of candidates and attract those who best match your needs—use the right mix of internal and external recruitment resources. When using external resources go for a long-term partnership so that your expert learns your company's unique recruitment needs and you can also evaluate the effectiveness of their support.

(5) Develop a recruitment workflow and identify the key players who would be involved in the process. A key part of this process is the interview(s)—this the big opportunity to really evaluate the potential employee, validate their competencies, skills and what they have on their resume and sell your company also. Many companies do not realize that candidates are interviewing them for the purpose of seeing whether the company is a fit for the candidate's goals and objectives!

(6) Be honest with the candidate about your company, the job opportunity, and the potential for employee development.

(7) Develop key metrics about your recruitment process, evaluate its effectiveness, and make adjustments necessary to achieve your goal of attracting the most suitable candidates for your company.

- *Retention*—When a company decides to hire people, the investment process starts immediately with the cost of time of recruitment staff, advertising, use of recruitment firms and interviewing etc. When a candidate is hired, the investment continues as the employee is educated, trained, coached, mentored, developed, and is paid in return through the compensation and benefits plan. Your company receives the return on that investment as the employee discharges their responsibilities as per their job description and fulfills their full performance potential. As each year goes by, the cumulative investment in that employee increases significantly, if that employee decides to leave when you need her expertise, this can be a real blow to the company. The appraisal and career development process is the formal process to keep a finger on the pulse of the employee. The process should be done throughout the year and should serve as the forum for both employer and employee to keep evaluating the value proposition on an ongoing basis—is the value creation mutually acceptable? When the value creation is one sided in the employee's favor, then the employer has to make adjustments to ensure that the company receives the value from the employee commensurate with the investment in the employee. The following choices are available to the employer in this situation:

(1) Attitude issues—seek to realign expectations honest discussions with the employee about what is expected and the consequences if expectations are not met.

(2) Lack of appropriate skills, knowledge and expertise—review employee skills and competencies and institute appropriate training if a gap is identified.

(3) Not the right fit for the company—in this situation you need to be decisive and end the relationship with an employee.

(4) Overstaffing situation—consider retraining and relocation to other areas of the company. In the event that you do have to downsize, do it in a way that will still allow the employee to view your company as a desirable place to work.

When the value creation is one-sided in favor of the company, this is an equally problematic situation. There are three scenarios that play themselves out every day in business as employees compare their performance with that of colleagues and feel that they are not fairly rewarded with compensation, benefits and career advancement opportunities:

(1) They can work harder in the hope that the manager recognizes the added effort and rewards them for it—this is a short-term solution and if the manager does not do something quickly, frustration sets in, and option 3 becomes more and more attractive to the employee.

(2) They can pull up on the hand brake and slow down because they feel that they are being used and not getting what is due to them—this is obviously a bad situation for both the company and the employee, no one wins here.

(3) Or they can decide that they have had enough an leave the organization—this is possibly the single most common way that companies lose their good resources, corporate knowledge, and potential for value creation.

It should be obvious from the preceding discussion that you retention strategy can be the difference between a high-performance organization and a mediocre or an even failed one.

- Succession planning strategies—the proactive organization is one that is always planning for change is the staffing needs of the organization. Vacant positions that are needed and go unfilled for an unusually long time or are filled with people who are not a proper match for the job is a one indication of poor succession planning. Vacancies arise for a variety of reasons:

  —*Normal attrition*—people have worked until retirement and are moving on to other personal challenges. It is easy to plan for this type of staffing change as most people work to asset date (usually 65 years) before retirement.

  —*Promotions, lateral moves, reassignment on projects*—these vacancies sometimes can create a void in the department or team that the employee leaves. Usually, this is an event that should be planned ahead of time and the manager generally is able to find a replacement.

  —*Resignations*—as discussed above, when employees feel that they are not realizing their full potential or feel that they are not treated fairly one option is for them to leave the organization. Resignations can be painful for the company especially if it comes as a surprise and the manager is unable to have a contingency plan in place for continuity of the operations.

  —*Firings*—when this is done in a reactive manner, there can be adverse consequences, such as possible litigation and unplanned vacancies that can disrupt the operations.

  —*Miscellaneous*—*illness, accidents, death etc.*—these events can all create vacancies that must be filled to ensure continuity of the operations and in general the company's business.

The goal of succession planning is to proactively plan and execute tactics so that there is minimum negative effect to the organization when employees leave the company, even if the event is unplanned. Many companies claim that they do succession planning and they can pull up a report immediately to show when staff is planning to or should retire. They are generally unable to show any strategy or planning on what they will do when the events occur. I call this "succession monitoring," not succession planning. A simple way to gauge how well you are doing succession planning is to ask anyone in the organization the questions: *Can you identify who will fill your position and do a good job if you are not in the organization tomorrow?* The answer to this question is generally—no! The following steps are necessary for succession planning:

(1) Ongoing staffing needs projections with scenario planning based on the possible events discussed above.

(2) Effective performance appraisal and career development with detailed learning agreements for each employee.

(3) An effective skill development program that aims to close any existing skill gaps and develop new skills in line with employee learning agreements.

(4) Create opportunities for employees to try out new skills through short stints in a higher position—e.g. fill short-term vacancies due to sick leave, vacation, project assignments.

(5) Develop apprentice, co-operative programs with colleges and universities to attract entry level employees and have a pool of interested entry level candidates.

(6) Document the costs and benefits of your succession planning strategy and show that there are real benefits to the organization from this process.

- *Skills development program*—Skill programs are often called "training" programs. They support succession planning and also provide the forum for employees to keep up with the skills needed to be effective in the ever-changing world of asset technology and new business processes. The steps in developing and maintaining an effective skills development program are shown below in Figure 7.3.

An effective skills development program is focused on developing the right skills and keeping them current for people to execute the various business processes around the asset lifecycle. Skills are linked to each responsibility, role, and ultimately to the job description of employees. Each skill should have an associated competency description. Once this

Training Program Design and Implementation

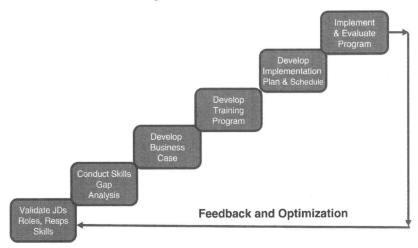

FIGURE 7.3 *Skills Development or Training Program.*

step is completed, it is possible to move to conducting a gap analysis—what skills do individual employees have and how do they compare with what is desired. This exercise can be quite revealing. You will identify the skills gaps needed to be filled for the various employees, and you will identify additional skills not currently needed but of future importance in career development and succession planning. It is to close any gaps identified. This can be general training that groups of employees attend, or it can be training focused on individual employees. Training can be for new skill development or can be refresher training where the skill is not used frequently enough for individuals to be competent. Skills development is not based on a single session. There should be ongoing evaluation of the program, links to performance appraisal, career development, and succession planning program, and regular adjustments to meet the needs of the operations. As with every program that requires an investment of funds, plus the time of human resources professionals and employees, it is important to track costs and benefits and demonstrate beyond any doubt that skills development program is essential to a sustainable organization.

- *Other areas focused on employee well-being*—an employee who is of sound mind, physical health and emotional stability, will be better prepared to do an effective job using the company's assets to create a product or service for the company's customers. Vibrant *Health and Safety, Fitness and Employee Assistance Programs* can be valuable in helping employees achieve the right balance needed to be effective at their jobs. It is also necessary to have an easy- to-read Employee Handbook with all the necessary guidelines and information needed to get things done in the organization and to meet the company's code of ethics and professionalism. This can be available in a hardcopy or can be accessible through the company's intranet.

When the above procedures are implemented, it is realistic to expect a high-performance organization where people demonstrate the following desired behaviors:

- Knowledge management is actively practiced resulting in corporate knowledge retention.
- Performance management drives effectiveness and decision making.
- The workforce practices workforce flexibility improving "wrench on bolt time."
- The workforce is multi-skilled, minimizing the number of personnel that are needed to do a job safely and effectively.
- People enjoy working creating value for the company and feel that they are fairly compensated in return.
- People actively pursue career development through use of learning agreements and the skills development program.
- Effective succession planning ensures that the right people with the right skills are always available to execute the company's business processes within the asset lifecycle.
- People embrace performance management as a concept that helps them and the company stay on top of the things they need to excel at for success.
- People are proud to be employees of the company and are active ambassadors for new recruits.
- People work in a team-based environment and are empowered to be creative, innovative and identify/execute continuous improvement initiatives that can keep the organization sustainable.

Corporate Knowledge Retention

Corporate knowledge is one of the key building blocks of

sustainability. It is the collective wisdom that keeps a company competitive and innovative in their particular business area and able to sustain a world-class stature. It is however, one of the most challenging issues for most companies and many end up with a mediocre performance or end up going out of business if this concept is not fully understood and practiced. Many companies are now bracing for the major exodus of baby boomers who are expected to retire in large numbers in the next decade, These employees (at all levels in the organization) will be leaving with most of the knowledge in their heads unless a deliberate effort is made to transfer that to other staff or have it captured in some medium. Acquiring the right knowledge, sharing it with those who need to know and continuously refining that knowledge are fundamental to a high-performance organization. Corporate knowledge is acquired over a number of years and is created and handed down by the people who work in the company. Some companies conduct mergers and acquisitions to increase its corporate knowledge and ensure competitiveness and sustainability. Unfortunately many people view corporate knowledge as intellectual property and the unique patents or trade secrets that give the company an edge on its competition. While this is very important there are many different types of knowledge that contribute to the company's profitability, high-performance as an organization and to sustainability. The additional focus areas are closely associated with the asset lifecycle. Companies that excel at knowledge management focus on all knowledge areas, creating, refining and sharing knowledge necessary to keep the company successful. Many companies are, however, vulnerable on many fronts in the area of corporate knowledge:

- *Knowledge areas are not defined and linked to the company's core business areas*—this is the fundamental building block of knowledge management. Knowledge areas must be clearly defined and must be associated with all business elements including the business processes for all phases of the asset lifecycle,
- *Knowledge is not secure and vulnerable to competitors*—Security is an issue receiving attention recently. Security breaches can be as simple as someone hacking into computer systems and stealing financial and sales information about clients. Or, they can be more sinister plots to steal trade secrets, drawings, and designs that are critical to a company's competitiveness. It is therefore necessary to categorize knowledge and apply the right levels of security for access and modifications. Employee loyalty, use of documents management systems, and implementing cyber

security technology and practices are some of the concepts that are being used to deal with this knowledge management issue.

- *Knowledge is of poor quality and unreliable*—Knowledge quality or its lack can be connected to the popular saying "Garbage In, Garbage Out." Many paper records and electronic databases contain vast collections of data. If this data is of poor quality and integrity, it cannot be relied on for conversion into information needed for error-free decision making. In many cases it is easier for companies to dump existing data and start from scratch, when new business applications are implemented.
- *Knowledge is stored in difficult-to-access media or not stored at all*—Numerous companies still depend on paper records. For those who have embraced technology without a clear framework and vision for knowledge management, there is the concern of duplication of data as it is re-entered into different systems for others to use. The objective of creating data once and having it used by anyone who needs it cannot be achieved in an environment such as this.
- *Most of the company's corporate knowledge is stored in people's heads—and it walks out when the employee leaves the company*—While this is a result of poor succession planning, it is still a major knowledge management challenge. Ideally, proper documentation and ongoing staff education and development for transferring corporate knowledge to others in the company would minimize the impact of employees leaving the organization. Some companies are actively encouraging networks of retired professionals to coach, mentor, and pass on knowledge to less experienced staff.
- *There are varying versions of the knowledge and it is interpreted differently by different groups or individuals*—Poor knowledge sharing, empire building, and poor communications are the main contributors of this problem. Sometimes in an organization where there is a number of creative and innovative people, individuals will modify existing knowledge to suit their views or unique requirements. They may even inject wholly new knowledge. If there are inadequate mechanisms to encourage knowledge sharing and management, you have failed to achieve the full potential of your organization.
- *Knowledge is hoarded for control*—Many people are scared to teach someone else their job for fear that they may end up losing their job to that individual or the individual will move up faster in the organization. This type of behavior results in a knowledge

environment that does not actively support the company's vision and mission.

In today's information economy, it is easier than ever to obtain and store data and information. The resulting information overload makes it difficult to access and deliver the right information quickly to the people who need it to be productive in their jobs. Without a well-designed knowledge management strategy, organizations can find themselves buried in facts and information, without the capability of translating them into effective decisions and actions. An effective knowledge management plan can directly improve and sustain your organization's competitiveness. Figure 7.4 shows the relationship among data, information, knowledge and decision making. Capturing the relevant raw data from your day-to-day transactions as you execute your business processes, creates the base data stock that you can draw on to create data subsets and information from queries. The resulting reports (word, spreadsheets, graphs etc.) constitute knowledge and drive decision making, as people interpret the information and form relationships based on theory, past experiences, or learned patterns. The result is ongoing value creation through continuous improvement of the operations.

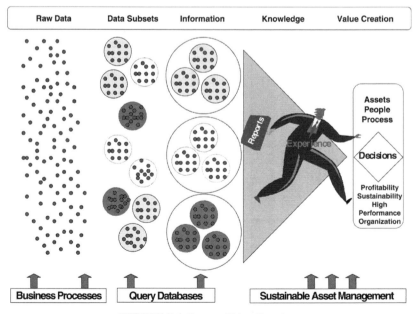

FIGURE 7.4 Data to Value Creation.

Knowledge Management (KM)

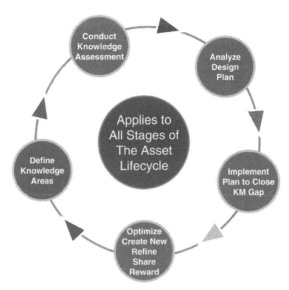

FIGURE 7.5 *Knowledge Management Circle.*

The foregoing sheds light on the need for corporate knowledge retention through effective knowledge management. It has not provided a framework for implementing such a concept. The recommended approach to corporate knowledge management is given in the knowledge management circle (Figure 7.5), which was discussed briefly in Chapter 6. It shows how your organization can develop a knowledge management plan and become effective at this important process. There are five steps to the knowledge management process:

- *Step 1—Define knowledge areas.* This step is a critical starting point for understanding what business you are in and what knowledge areas you need to excel at to be successful and sustain a high level of performance. The following categories of knowledge should be analyzed and documented:

  —Intellectual knowledge that gives you company a clear edge in the market e.g. this can be trade secrets and patents this is usually well defined and secured. This type of knowledge is directly related to asset management as it often relates to unique asset design or business processes.

—Financial performance and planning knowledge.

—Client databases that contain valuable information necessary to retain and continue to increase your target market as your company target increasing customer satisfaction.

—Business process related data, e.g., asset data—drawings, bill of materials, maintenance and operating procedures, specifications, work and cost history.

—Asset-related knowledge associated with design, performance, and overall condition.

—People related data—skills, qualifications, training, career development plans.

—Tacit knowledge—stored in head of employees and refers to information they have accumulated over time to solve problems and make their jobs easier.

—Strategic planning knowledge from environmental scanning that helps keep your company ahead of the competition.

- *Step 2—Conduct a knowledge assessment.* When knowledge areas are defined, you can now conduct an assessment of how well you perform in each of the areas. It is important that the assessment process starts with education and orientation around knowledge management to relevant staff. This should smooth the way for the assessment without creating unnecessary road blocks or apprehension in employees. A communication plan about the intended knowledge management program can be a good start in this area. This opportunity gap then needs to be translated into a business case for implementing a proper knowledge management program. This step requires evaluation of the above knowledge categories based on the following criteria:

—What data do we have?

—Where and how is it stored?

—How is data currently linked to knowledge management and decision making?

—Is knowledge protected from loss through staff turnover, disasters, or theft?

—What is the quality of that knowledge—is it reliable?

—Are the appropriate levels of security applied for access, changes, and sharing?

—Is knowledge easily accessible to those who need it to do their jobs effectively?

—Is there a process to continuously update/refine existing knowledge?

—Is there a process to create new knowledge necessary for sustainability of the company?

—How is the knowledge process managed?

—How does the organization support knowledge management—is it clear in job descriptions, roles, responsibilities and in the organization structure?

—Is there a rewards and recognition system in place to encourage creativity and innovation in the knowledge development?

—How does your company corporate knowledge compare with best in class companies in your business environment?

- *Step 3—Analyze, design and develop an action plan to close any gaps identified.* This step develops all the tactical detail to make knowledge management an effective business process for your company. This step builds directly from the results of Step 1, and the following activities are required to build an effective plan:

  —Develop a gap analysis with supporting findings, conclusions, and recommendations.

  —Develop a compelling business case for a knowledge management program.

  —Secure approval from senior management for funding and implementation of the program.

  —Develop a detailed action plan with tasks, resourcing, milestones and deliverables and benefits tracking.

  —Communicate the plan to all to gain buy-in from all staff in the company.

- *Step 4—Implement the action plan to close the gap.* This requires the necessary funding, resources, and appropriate implementation team to take the action plan to reality. Apply sound project management and change management strategies to guarantee a successful implementation. Implement benefits tracking and use this to consolidate gains for the program. Implementation should focus on the knowledge management business processes at which the company should excel, the people requirements to execute the business processes flawlessly, and the technology assets needed to enable the knowledge management process (discussed below).

- *Step 5—Optimize.* Keep on creating new knowledge, refine existing knowledge and share knowledge with everyone who needs to know to do their job effectively. Ensure that rewards and recognition follow for those who are passionate about knowledge management.

A key aspect of corporate knowledge retention and knowledge management is the huge challenge of managing data in a world that is overwhelmed with data. Before the advent of the computer and its immense data storage and processing capabilities, companies that practiced knowledge management used paper records. This was easy to do in the early stages of the company, but each year brought more history: sales, accounting, asset, human resources etc. Retrieving information became a major challenge and in fact most employees will attest to the fact they are not too motivated to sift through reams of paper unless it will have a direct impact on them personally. Contrary to popular opinion in the eighties and nineties, technology has not made things better. Many companies are struggling to manage the deluge of data that has been made possible by the information age. Successful companies have recognized the relationship between data, information and knowledge and sustainability of their business. They have learnt to understand what data is relevant to their business, capture it electronically (as far as possible), shape it into information, interpret it based on intellectual capacity, share it with anyone who needs to use it to do their jobs effectively and continuously refine it as the business environment changes. Figure 7.6 gives high level overview of how an integrated technology asset solution can support corporate knowledge retention. Essentially, this integrated technology asset enables business processes, creates data (dynamic and static) and allows for that data to be easily mined, queried, sorted and interpreted to drive decision making key to survival or sustainability of your company. This concept will be discussed in detail in Chapter 8—Enabling Technologies for Asset Management.

Deliverables from a corporate knowledge management program (based on the Knowledge management Circle):

- *Step 1*—Definition of knowledge areas for business excellence and sustainability—this includes templates and formats for each knowledge category.
- *Step 2*—Opportunity gap, conclusions on how knowledge management and corporate knowledge retention are practiced by the company, choices for the company to close the gap, and capitalize on the opportunities and a sound business case from getting the green light for implementation.
- *Step 3*—Detailed implementation plan to develop an effective KM process and close opportunity gaps—this should provide all tasks and sub tasks with associated timing, costs, (resources—internal or external, hardware, technology assets, services to create the

Integrated Technology Supports Asset Management

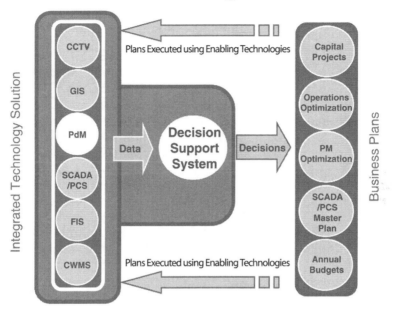

FIGURE 7.6 *Integrated Technology Supports Corporate Knowledge Retention.*

integrated technology asset solution and costs needed to operate and maintain the system), milestones, and detailed description of deliverables.

- *Step 4*—Implementation of KM Process, Integrated Technology Solution and tracking of results. Implementation should follow the project management process focusing on time, scope, money and impact of the existing operations.
- *Step 5*—Culture of knowledge optimization—creating new, refining existing, rewards and recognition for those who actively participate in Knowledge management. This behavior must be anchored in the company's culture to ensure ongoing corporate knowledge retention.

Performance Management

We have heard the old sayings "What gets measured gets done" and

"Without data you are just another opinion" many times and they may seem to may be simplistic but has real meaning in the business environment. The best of strategic plans and intentions can amount to very little unless there are clear goals, objectives and associated targets to ensure that strategies for success are being achieved. We actually do practice performance management in our personal life for example financial planning to buy that new car, house or saving up to send the kids to college. The basic approach is to be clear on the vision or end state in terms of key indicators or behaviors, understand what the current situation is, develop the road map to achieve the vision and the key indicators or behaviors at key stages of the journey. Performance management in a company is essentially the same approach but with a wider focus and on more complex business processes. Understanding the end vision, setting targets that are realistic and managing performance and expectations around these targets is essentially the practice of Performance Management. The balanced scorecard approach shown in Figure 7.7, modified to fit the philosophy of optimization through—Assets, People and Processes, is a robust framework for performance management. It is also tied directly to the concept of the triple bottom line ensuring that the company has an economic, social and environmental balanced focus on its operations. It should be applied at the corporate level in the organization and implemented in a consistent manner to the front line teams. In the balanced scorecard approach to performance management, performance is managed in four key areas:

- *Customers*—how do we want our external customers to see us in the areas of quality, cost, responsiveness, social and environmental responsibility?
- *Financial*—overall return on all assets employed in the production of goods or services. We must be able to visualize how we must appear to our shareholders or the public if we are succeeding financially. For many companies this can be interpreted simply as increasing shareholder wealth and at the same time continuing to invest in assets and people resources.
- *People*—are our people learning and growing with us, are we developing agility and flexibility necessary to change and continuously improve? Are we leveraging our people to capture, share, and create the knowledge necessary to keep the company sustainable?
- *Processes*—To maximize the return on our assets and satisfy our customers (internal & external) what business processes must we excel at? How do we know that we are excelling at these business

Performance Management Using the Balanced Scorecard Approach

FIGURE 7.7 *Performance Management Using the Balanced Scorecard.*

processes? The business processes around the asset lifecycle are obvious ones we should excel at, however, other business processes such as strategic planning, marketing, public relations, community development etc. are just as important.

Performance management is closely associated with the strategic planning process discussed in Chapter 6. The following are the main links to the strategic planning process:

- During the visioning step, a corporate scorecard is developed for the strategies critical to the success of the company. The corporate scorecards should be based on the triple bottom line and the balanced scorecard performance management concept. Strategic goals and objectives should be linked to measurable and realistic targets that can be used by the executive management team to get a feel for the performance of the company.

- The result is distilled further with the input of a wide cross-section of staff at the business unit level to create the business-unit-level scorecard with its measures and targets.
- Further refinement to the frontline team level results in simple team scorecards that are tied directly to corporate goals and objectives and have their own measures and targets.
- Monitoring, trending, feedback and adjustments to plans support your vision of sustainability.

In this way everyone in the company is clear on how their jobs link to the company's corporate goals, objectives (and to its vision and mission) and what they must do as a team and individually for the company to be successful and to sustain high performance.

Deliverables when implementing a Performance Management program:

- Corporate Balanced Scorecard
- Business Units Balanced Scorecards
- Frontline Teams balanced scorecards
- Technology solution for creating, tracking and managing the respective metrics
- Training on performance management
- Documentation on the performance management process

APPENDIX 7.1 *(see p. 149)*

REFERENCES

1. "Organizational behavior," Professor Robert Dailey, *Financial Times Management,* 1998.
2. *Balanced Scorecard, Translating Strategy Into Action,* Kaplan and Norton, 1996.

APPENDIX 7.1—SAMPLE PUBLIC WORKS ORGANIZATION DESIGN THAT SUPPORTS SUSTAINABLE ASSET MANAGEMENT

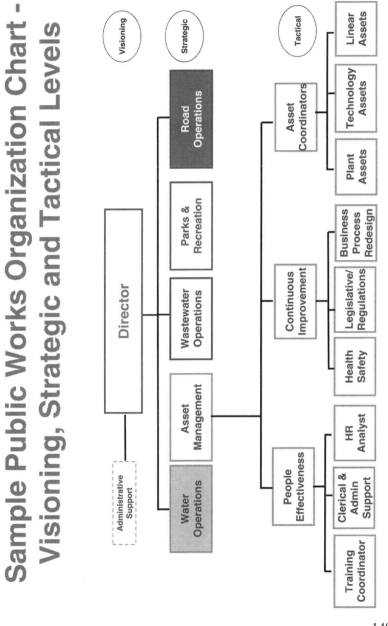

Sample Public Works Organization Chart – Visioning, Strategic and Tactical Levels

CHAPTER 8

Integrated Technology Asset Solution

ENABLING TECHNOLOGIES FOR SUSTAINABLE ASSET MANAGEMENT

Technology is the underlying reason for change in many areas. Hardware and software should be considered as valuable assets to be managed. Technology has been the most important driver for productivity gains in the last 20 years and is also one of the key enablers of asset management. The biggest contribution to sustainability is data for creation of corporate knowledge. Although a very valuable output from an integrated technology asset solution, data can overwhelm. For some companies the data is of poor quality and integrity and is not trusted. Many informal and often unapproved methods exist to get work done without using the technology provided. Here are current technology trends that affect asset management:

(1) Rapid increase in computing power (CPU processing speed) as defined by Moore's law. As computers become faster and are able to process more complex algorithms so too will business software be able to perform ever more complex computations.

(2) Cheap and large volumes of storage space will allow the capture and storage of much more data than what is possible today

(3) Miniaturization of hardware will result in complete business applications operating on handheld devices, allowing use of these systems by field staff. Continued developments in computer hardware that fits into headsets will enable workers to have both hands free and at the same time have access to vital information for troubleshooting and repairing assets.

(4) Improvements in wireless technology will allow handhelds to communicate with main servers as well as microprocessors embedded in assets.

(5) Voice recognition will influence how end-users interact with business applications. Vendors will actively pursue this technology to minimize the age-old problem of end-users' unwillingness to use the keyboard for data entry.

(6) The Internet will continue to revolutionize how software is deployed and accessed and at the same time provide key links to other valuable information sites necessary to support effective work management. The Internet will also be the method of choice for delivering software and upgrades from the vendor (instead of the shipment of CDs as happens today).

(7) Standardization of programming languages and software design guidelines will eventually force business application vendors to adopt a common approach to design of their products. This will drive vendors to differentiate their product by adding more complex functionality, improving service levels and offering attractive prices just to get new customers. The clients will benefit in the long run due to standardization by being able to easily replace their business application if the vendor goes out of business or if they have a pressing business need to move to another system.

There are many business applications and various designs of hardware and networking configurations. Selecting and implementing the right solution for your company is a daunting task. The situation becomes even more challenging after a solution is put in place, to keep up with continued changes in technologies. In this chapter we discuss the relationship between asset management and technology. The chapter presents a structured approach for selecting and implementing the most appropriate integrated technology solution for your business and provides guidance on how to be proactive in dealing with ongoing advances in technology.

Asset Management and the Enabling Integrated Technology Solution (ITS)

We have shown that all of a company's business processes can be linked in one way or another to individual or multiple asset lifecycle phases. Advances in computer technology have made it possible to enhance these business processes or replace them entirely with computer programs. For example, instead of physically visiting a production process, manually adjusting the process, and monitoring system performance, it is now possible through the use of Process Control System (PCS) and Supervisory Control and Data Acquisition (SCADA) systems to control the operations and capture/trend production data remotely. This can be done over vast geographic distances; indeed, it is now possible for doctors to remotely perform surgeries on patients and for IT staff to remotely diagnose and fix problems on your computer.

The ITS is derived from the asset lifecycle (Figure 8.1). Developing the right ITS starts with a complete understanding of the business processes that you need to excel at in order to be competitive. A definition of the business processes will yield workflows, the asset data model that forms the foundation of the ITS, the functional, technical requirements and interface specifications for the first release of the ITS.

Workflow

This type of information is the engine for various business applications and essentially provides the roadmap for the flow of transactions from initiation to completion. For example, in the case of the CWMS it can be

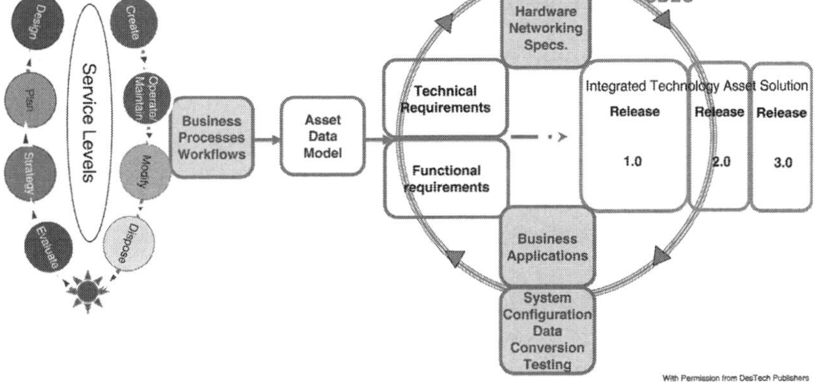

FIGURE 8.1 *The ITS is Derived From the Asset Lifecycle.*

a central workplace (workflow headquarters) through which all actions, messages, special reports and functionality of the various modules is located. In this regard, workflow should: provide for electronic approvals (manual or automatic) based on user- defined criteria, send automatic messages when key events occur prompting the user to carry out a specific action, and send Email messages (again manual or automatic) needed to support the work process. Many business applications have a built-in workflow engine for all transactions within the application. In the ITS, it is necessary to build another level of workflow to allow data to move among applications, This concept can be easily captured in the interface definition and subsequent programming.

Asset Data Model

A major challenge for IT staff in developing an ITS is ownership of asset-related data. Every business application has its own database, and if it is directly related to enabling transactions over the asset lifecycle, it will have its own asset records. To compound matters, different organizational units tend to have ownership for different areas of the asst lifecycle and there are unique business applications for work involved in these lifecycle phases. Naturally, these organizational units want to own the asset data that is stored in the business application database. For example, a process control system will refer to the same assets that a computerized work management system and a geographical information system refer to. Generally, there are different numbering systems for the same assets in the different systems. During the normal course of operations people will do work and make changes to update the asset records in each database. When this process is not carefully managed, the data in the different records for the same asset are not in synch. Organizations spend a lot of time trying to put in place systems that enable manual update of the different asset records. There is always a lag time involved and a higher probability of data-entry errors. An example of this, is work being done by repair crews on a water distribution system. They make changes to the asset configuration (clamp a leaking line, change out a section of pipe or relocate a valve). Both the Computerized Work Management and the Geographical Information Systems need to have the updated information on the linear asset that was worked on. In practice, a hand sketch of the changes is stapled to a paper copy of the work order and sent by mail to the GIS clerk for update to the asset record in the GIS. The same information is stored as a text description in the work order history for the asset in the CWMS.

The solution lies in the design of the ITS and the use of a common asset registry (Figure 8.2), which is the owner of all information on the asset. As people use their business applications to carry out responsibilities over the asset lifecycle, the applications automatically send updates to the master record of the asset in the asset registry. If there are changes in the master record because of work done in another business application, then the asset registry (after it has been updated with these changes) will publish these changes to other business applications that need the update. In this way all systems will be up-to-date and in synch with the master records of the various assets they manage. The company will also have one repository of the master asset records.

Functional Requirements

Functional requirements are the configurations and transactions that allow the execution of business processes. These requirements vary based on the business processes for the unique aspects of the asset lifecycle for which the business unit is responsible. For example, in the *evaluation* phase a business planning unit will need modeling software; similarly the engineering business unit will seek to have the best com-

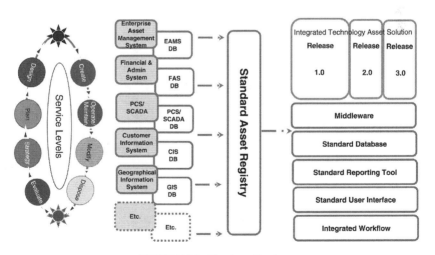

FIGURE 8.2 *The Asset Registry.*

puter-aided design business application. In order to select and implement the most appropriate business application, it is necessary to define the functional requirements to execute the various business processes. A brief overview of the various business applications and high level functionality that are available today is given in Appendix 8.1. Sample functional requirements for a CWMS are provided in Appendix 8.2.

Technical Requirements

Technical requirements determine how the business applications operate in a technical environment. Here it is necessary to define the hardware (wide- and local-area network designs, servers, desktops, laptops, mobile devices etc.), networking (fiber optics, wireless), databases, and operating system requirements. Decisions made at this stage are very significant to the overall ITS. The choice of an operating system and database could potentially limit your choice of business applications, because some vendors design their system to work with specific databases and operating systems. This is slowly becoming less of a problem as vendors are now trying to ensure that their systems can work with the more popular operating systems and databases. Developing clear standards for the technical requirements of the ITS is a good asset management practice that will become very useful in the subsequent release process necessary to manage the ITS. A sample technical requirement is given in Appendix 8.3.

Interface Specifications

The third set of requirements for the ITS is the definition of the flow of data among the different business applications. They also spell out the interface technical environment. For example, if a middleware approach is used to link the business applications, then the requirements for the middleware must be clearly defined. In designing the interface framework, the following business and technology principles should be considered:

- Business-driven
- Buy vs. build
- Mainstream applications
- Open standards
- Standardization
- Re-usability
- Reliability

- Maintainability
- Integrity

Successful integration requires:

- Availability of the supplier of the data required by the consumer
- Ability of the data to be transformed appropriately for the consumer
- Agreement on exactly what data will be exchanged
- Ability of the supplier to meet the time requirements of the consumer
- Coherent handling of errors and exception conditions

There are four approaches to interface design:

(1) Direct application to application links (most commonly used—potentially most expensive approach over the long run)—Figure 8.3

(2) An integration database (commonly used and better understood, moderate to high upfront costs)—Figure 8.4

Direct Interface API to API Approach

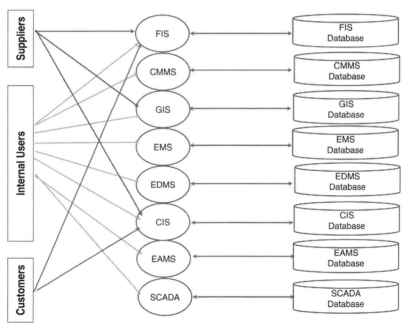

FIGURE 8.3 *API to API approach to Integration.*

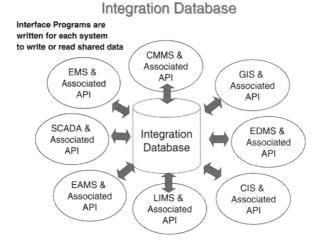

FIGURE 8.4 *The Integration Database.*

(3) Integration Bus (more commonly used outside of the public sector, higher costs upfront, requires some technical knowledge to support but potentially least costly option in the long run)—Figure 8.5.

(4) Object broker approach (least commonly used, requires advanced technical knowledge and still theoretical)

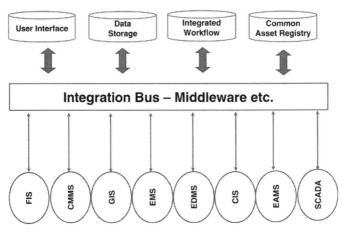

FIGURE 8.5 *The Integration Bus.*

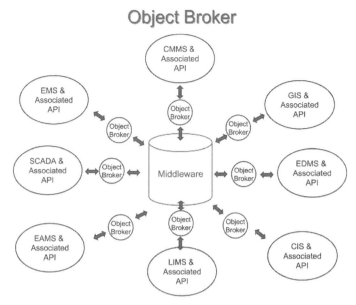

FIGURE 8.6 *The Object Broker.*

SELECTING AND IMPLEMENTING THE COMPONENTS OF THE ITS

Recognizing that you need expert help in selecting and implementing the various components of your ITS can be an important step towards success. The challenge is to ensure that the right mix or your resources and external resources are used, and you remain in control. The knowledge-transfer concept (Figure 8.7) is recommended as a method to keep a project moving along at a reasonable pace and at the same time transfer knowledge to your staff to ensure sustainability of the ITS.

SELECTING BUSINESS APPLICATIONS FOR THE ITS

The next step is to find suitable business applications and vendor partners for the ITS. The following selection process (Figure 8.8) can be used for selecting all of the applications necessary to enable your business processes. A summarized description of the six-step selection process is given below. (A more detailed description can be found in the book *Computerized Work Management Systems for Utilities and Plant Operations,* Lutchman, 2004).

Step 1—Planning Phase—Select Internal Team Members, Consultant and Project Kick-off

The first step in the process, after the need for the business application and its justification are completed, is to acquire the right consulting resources to partner on your project. It would be advisable to consider retaining this resource for the entire selection and implementation phases of the project. This means defining the scope of the services required, developing a request for proposal (RFP) for consulting services, and selecting a suitable candidate. Sometimes it is possible to select a consultant without having to go through a competitive process if it can be shown that the candidate is uniquely qualified and has good references. Once the consultant is engaged, the first responsibility is to work with the project sponsor to determine the best internal team members to form part of the selection team. This group must have all the skill sets necessary to successfully select a consultant to partner on the project as well as be able to understand all aspects of the current business processes. Once the team is established, team members are provided with background information on the project (business case expected results and high-level project plan). High-level orientation on the selection and implementation process, as well as best practice concepts applicable to work, asset, operations and materials management, are a great way to provide the basic orientation to the team. The team can now complete the planning process

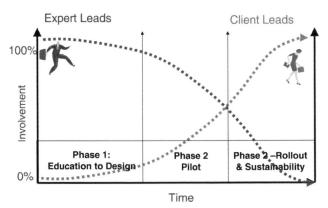

FIGURE 8.7 *Concept of Knowledge Transfer to the Client.*

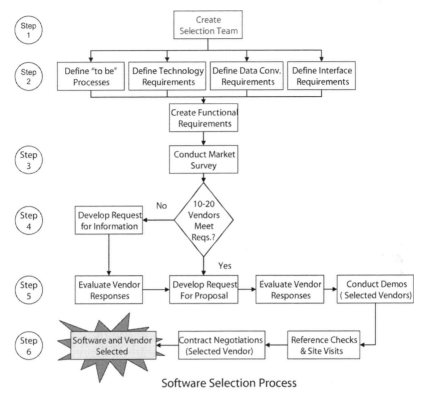

Software Selection Process

FIGURE 8.8 *Selection Process.*

by developing a project plan for the selection phase and the detailed communication plan for the project ensuring that the right message, the intended audience, the communication medium, the frequency of communication, and the feedback mechanism are all established in advance.

Step 2—The Market Survey

The market survey is the first step in the process to help make sense out of the many systems in the market. It is also a step that can be done instead of the RFI Step 3 if you have an experienced consultant helping you in the selection process. It is first necessary to understand the high-level functionality you need to support your business needs, the general system size (number of users, expected data requirements), desired database, operating system, and some criteria around the desired vendor with whom you would like to partner. Based on this information, it is usually possible to identify 10 to 20 vendors who appear able to meet your requirements. The sources of information about these companies can be from the consultant's database of vendors, the Internet, and other software information sources. If a market survey is conducted instead of an RFI, it is possible to reduce the selection time by at least 6 to 8 weeks.

Step 3—The Request for Information (RFI) and the Scoring Process

In the event the market survey is not considered (based on fears of litigation from vendors who may think they were not given a fair chance to bid) or the survey does not produce an adequate list of vendors, then the RFI process must be followed. Essentially, the RFI goes out to all vendors through print media and on your company website in an effort to attract as much interest as possible. In addition, your consultant should have a sense of the vendors and products that would match your needs and should be able to develop a list of 10 to 15 vendors to which the RFI should be sent. You'll want to ensure that these vendors do in fact see your RFI. Highly detailed specifications will help ensure that only vendors who really think that they are a match for your requirements will respond. The objective at this stage is to identify at least 10 vendors who should move on to the RFP phase of the selection process. RFI responses should then be evaluated and scored to reduce the number of vendors to 5 or 6 for the RFP process.

Step 4—The Request for Proposal (RFP)

The RFP phase of the selection process is the most intensive and time-consuming phase of the selection process. There are four key activities associated with this phase of work:

(1) Preparing the detailed functional and technical requirements for the system
(2) Building a thorough RFP document
(3) The bidder's meeting
(4) Evaluating the technical and cost proposals

A scoring spreadsheet can be used to translate the responses to the RFP's technical requirements into a quantitative score. Each functionality (or requirement) is given a rating (based on priority) and also an importance for weighting. A weighted score (rating multiplied by importance) can then be computed for each requirement. A subtotal by section and grand total for each bidder can then be computed and analyzed to determine the ranking of bidders. This ranking is important to determine who should proceed to the product demonstration phase. Usually the top 2 to 3 vendors and products are selected for this phase.

Step 5—The Product Demonstration

Product demonstration is critical to validating that vendor's response to the RFP, to evaluating how well the vendor meets your partnership requirements, and to perceiving the robustness and user-friendliness of the system. It is essential that you give the vendor adequate instructions and time to prepare for the product demonstration. Clear instructions in the form of a demonstrations script should elaborate the business processes to be enabled by the business application. A scoring system should be prepared to evaluate the demonstration phase. Scoring is based on:

- Validation of system functionality
- Ease of use and robustness
- Implementation methodologies
- Ability to meet your partnership requirements

Step 6—Reference Evaluation and Contract Negotiations

There are a number of important preparatory activities to set the stage for the contract negotiations step. A phone interview should be conducted with all of the references the vendors have identified in the RFP. At times, based on the comfort level with the vendor, it may be necessary to visit a reference site and observe the system being used in a live situation. If everything checks out favorably, it is necessary to draw up a contract that set the stages for a long and successful partnership with the vendor. You should seek legal advice to evaluate the software license and ensure that all dollar items, payment schedules, warranties, vendor personnel, scope items and schedules are clearly defined. It is advisable to have face-to-face discussions with the vendor at this stage, where counsel or a consultant might be present.

ITS IMPLEMENTATION PROCESS

A standard implementation process is recommended for any component of the ITS. The five step process shown in Figure 8.9 can be used for implementing individual business applications, major hardware changes and interfaces. A summarized description of the five-step implementation process is given below.

Step 1—Preplanning

The activities in the Pre-planning phase are: planning for change, developing the work plan, communications, develop supporting organization, develop hardware infrastructure, define "To Be" work processes and preliminary data collection.

Step 2—Conference Room Pilot

The Conference Room Pilot (CRP) is the term used to describe the phase of system development and testing prior to a field trial of the software with real users. In this phase, the implementation core team reviews the project plan from the pre-planning phase and creates the necessary detail to manage this phase effectively. There are a number of key activities involved in the CRP phase of implementation:

(1) Setup conference room pilot area step
(2) Load CWMS software and create database instances
(3) Core team training
(4) Configure software
(5) Data collection and conversion
(6) Define and build interfaces
(7) Conduct system testing

At the end of the CRP all configuration parameters should be exported into the development database in preparation for the field-trial phase of implementation. This should only be done when the core team is confident that the system configuration is acceptable, and testing has revealed the software is stable and robust.

Step 3—Field trial Phase

Some work has already been done on the field-trial area in the previous phases—it was selected in the Pre-planning phase and some employees were exposed to the software in the CRP phase. It is now time to develop the production database for the field trial area in preparation for going

Implementation Process for Business Applications

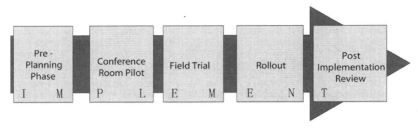

FIGURE 8.9 *Implementation Process.*

live with the business application. The activities in the field trial process are given below:

(1) Data collection, conversion and migration
(2) Preparation of end user training materials
(3) Set up end users
(4) End-user training
(5) Go live preparation and going live

Step 4—Rollout

Once the field trial is underway and performing well, the Core Team should start directing their attention to the Rollout phase of implementation with the goal of duplicating the field trial successes in all areas of the Company's operations. The steps in the rollout phase are very similar to the field trial but on a much larger scale. Rollout of the business application to the various other business units can be done on a sequential or phased basis, or resources permitting, a big bang approach can be done for all areas at one time. The activities in the rollout phase are given below:

(1) Prepare detailed rollout plan
(2) Prepare data collection/conversion plan
(3) Update system configuration
(4) Install hardware infrastructure
(5) Train end users
(6) Go Live preparation and support

Step 5—The Post-Implementation Review

The last step in the implementation process is to conduct a post-implementation review (PIR). This is often the step never carried out by most companies. Many assume that everything will be fine once you switch on the system and go live. It is important to seek a behavior of continuous improvement and reinforce new and desired behaviors. The PIR should be conducted by a small group of individuals selected from the core team and user groups. Your consultant should facilitate the PIR. The PIR is a key step in the change process to ensure that you are able to reap the benefits from the IITS investment. The activities in the PIR are given below:

(1) Review configuration
(2) Interview end users
(3) Review system use
(4) Review system performance
(5) Review data quantity and quality
(6) Present report to steering team
(7) Implement recommendations

Managing the Integrated Technology Asset—Keeping Current on Your Integrated Technology Asset Solution

The ITS can be viewed as another asset (in fact it may be many times costlier than most of your existing assets) and should be managed around the asset lifecycle in a similar fashion:

Needs Identification—required to improve productivity, manage the work process and asset management cost effectively and support corporate knowledge retention.

Plan and Evaluate—like any other critical asset, good planning and evaluation are important for this major investment. It requires careful understanding of your needs, involvement of all key players, developing a business case and selling the program to executive sponsors.

Design—this phase requires a full understanding of what is required of the software (functional requirements), how it fits into your current hardware and software technology environment (technical requirements), and how it supports your physical work environment (fixed and/or mobile access). In addition, it is essential to define what you expect from the business partnership with the potential vendors over the life of this important asset.

Purchase/Create/Implement—a solid selection and implementation process is critical to identifying the vendor and product that best meets your business needs. As with a physical asset, all the key players must work together for a good selection decision. Similarly the appropriate involvement of your personnel (end users and support groups) with the right mix of consulting and vendor support is also key to a successful implementation.

Commissioning—as with commissioning of any major asset, good planning and "Go Live" preparation are critical to success. Rigorous system testing in the implementation phase, effective and timely training of end-users, detailed check sheets and checks, a good support system (help desk), and a good communication plan for going live are necessary to make it through commissioning with minimal problems. The decision to run an old system in parallel for some time or shut down and start using the new system immediately would be one of the major decisions at this stage.

Operate and Maintain—operating and maintaining the ITS should be given the same level of importance and attention as you would to a critical physical asset. You need to ensure that the asset is used properly in support of our business practices and that you get the return on the investment identified at the "Planning and Evaluation" phase. You need to work closely with your vendor(s) to ensure that systems issues are addressed promptly with little impact on your end-users. Minor system upgrades or patches should be done transparently to the end-users. The goal is ensure that your practices are properly set up in the ITS; end-users see the system as an enabling tool, and all data is of high quality and integrity.

Modify or Upgrade—if you are doing a good job of keeping track of this asset's ability to meet your business needs you would always know if you were current on your system. The decision to upgrade to another release or make some programming changes (or add interfaces to other business systems) should be based on a sound rationale and should be planned and implemented using the system development lifecycle approach (Figure 8.10). *Note:* this approach should also be employed for making major configuration changes and applying patches to the system). This is discussed further below.

Decommission—as in the case of any asset, there comes a time the asset outlives its usefulness and must be replaced, in the case of the components of the ITS it can be premature (because of market forces—mergers/acquisitions), vendor going bankrupt or obsolete technology. It is important that you are doing ongoing scanning of the technology environment to be aware of these changes and be prepared to replace different ITS components.

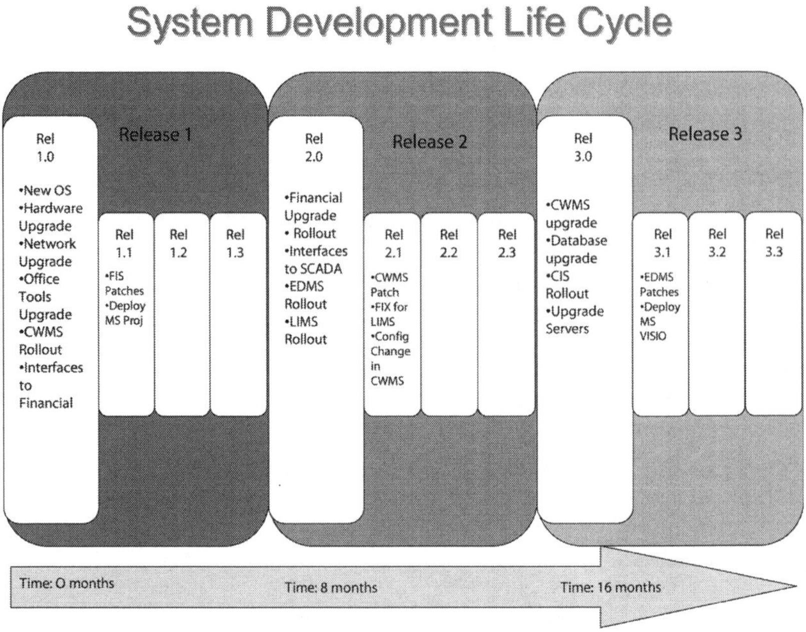

System Development Life Cycle

	Release 1				Release 2				Release 3		
Rel 1.0				**Rel 2.0**				**Rel 3.0**			
•New OS •Hardware Upgrade •Network Upgrade •Office Tools Upgrade •CWMS Rollout •Interfaces to Financial				•Financial Upgrade • Rollout •Interfaces to SCADA •EDMS Rollout •LIMS Rollout				•CWMS upgrade •Database upgrade •CIS Rollout •Upgrade Servers			
	Rel 1.1 •FIS Patches •Deploy MS Proj	**Rel 1.2**	**Rel 1.3**		**Rel 2.1** •CWMS Patch •FIX for LIMS •Config Change in CWMS	**Rel 2.2**	**Rel 2.3**		**Rel 3.1** •EDMS Patches •Deploy MS VISIO	**Rel 3.2**	**Rel 3.3**

Time: O months	Time: 8 months	Time: 16 months

FIGURE 8.10 *Staying Current on Your ITS.*

Replace—replacing your ITS components should be given the same effort and attention as when you first selected and implemented the specific components.

SYSTEM DEVELOPMENT LIFECYCLE

The system development lifecycle (Figure 8.10) approach to managing the ITS allows you to be proactive in applying new releases, updates of the various business applications, database and operating systems in manageable chunks. In addition, you can include any significant internal changes to the configuration of the various business applications in one of the step changes in a particular release. The idea of a working committee to proactively manage the changes that affect the integrated technology solution should be considered. This committee should be charged with developing a clear team charter with its vision and mission focused on development and the implementation of plans to always have a current integrated technology solution and minimize the risk to the company's business due to external technology factors. Managing software in this manner gives you the insurance and peace of mind that your company's critical business operations can survive the demise of one of your business software vendors. The approach, however, does not enable you to pick up signs of distress in your vendor's operations early enough to take appropriate action. In addition, you are also very reactive and unable to influence the process for updates and new releases of the various business applications from the vendors. You can be able to better deal with these areas if you get actively involved in the vendors' user groups and their annual conference.

THE ITS DRIVES ASSET MANAGEMENT RELATED DECISION MAKING

The ITS is now designed, selected, implemented and managed. We need to get the most value on a daily basis from this important and expensive asset. You need to ensure that all staff fully utilize the various enabling strategies as they execute the various business plans around the asset lifecycle. You need to ensure that staff actively leverages data to create knowledge that drives decision making (Figure 8.11). The ITS is one of the most valuable assets your company has invested in. It can provide you with the intelligence to drive continuous improvement and

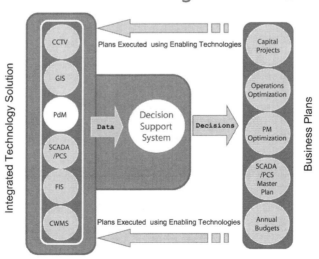

FIGURE 8.11 ITS Supports Knowledge Management and Decision Making.

sustainability. It can help you navigate the difficult times associated with potential loss of corporate knowledge associated with staff turnover. Finally, the ITS can create the quantum leaps in productivity necessary to stay competitive and sustain a high-performance organization.

APPENDIX 8.1

Many business applications have been developed to simplify and enable the various business processes around the asset lifecycle. Programmers and software developers are very busy at this time leveraging the continuous changes in technology and developing new and better applications. The graphic below (Figure 8.12) gives a listing of the more common applications that are used by companies as they carry out their daily activities:

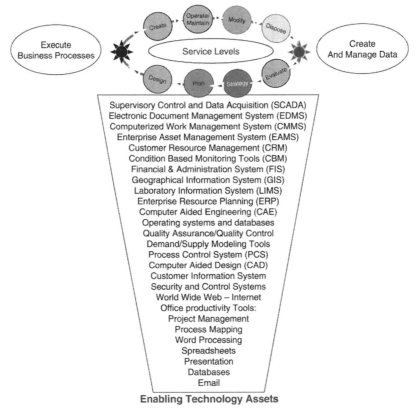

Enabling Technology Assets

FIGURE 8.12 Business Applications Around the Asset Lifecycle.

APPENDIX 8.2—SAMPLE KEY FUNCTIONAL REQUIREMENTS FOR AN ASSET MANAGEMENT SYSTEM (AMS)

The AMS should provide functionality in regards to set up and editing of performance centers and asset records in an asset registry for discrete, linear and virtual assets.
Asset numbering based on the Company's numbering standard (e.g. shown in Chapter 9).
Asset classification system based on asset categories and sub categories example Category—Pipe, Sub Category—PVC (see Chapter 9 for additional examples).
Assign asset criticality based on the Asset Management standard for criticality.
Fields that allow data entry for Original Equipment Manufacturer, Serial Number, Date Purchased, Date Installed, Commissioning Information.
Allow the set up of problem symptom, and reason for failure codes tied to the asset category.
Provide the ability to plot asset health statistics and provide a graphical representation of deterioration curves based on each or a combination of these parameters.
Allow for the set up of text description, operating manuals, BOM, specifications and drawings associated with the asset.
Allow the set up of geo-spatial data (X, Y coordinates) for asset tracking and location.
Allow the set up of all individuals responsible for maintaining the asset e.g. planner, scheduler, and manager.
Provide a graphical display as well as a tabular representation of the relationship with the asset and its parent processes or performance centers as well as its components.
Provide the ability to associate General Ledger account information for each asset.

(continued)

Allow the set up Preventive Maintenance jobs and associated triggering information against the asset.
Allow the set up of a security level rating for the asset and related routine security checks.
Allow for the use of RFID technology to locate, track PM work due and work history on asset.
Provide the ability to associate work related permits (such as hot work or excavation permit) with an asset.
Provide the ability to attach unlimited files to the asset through the use of Object Linking and Embedding (OLE) technology.
Provide editing capability for asset records such as copy, delete, make active/inactive, replacement etc.
Provide the ability to drill down to and access all related information from the asset record by drilling down on related fields e.g. Work and Cost History, BOM, POs, Permits, Drawings.
Allow simulation of asset replacement, modifications or upgrade type decisions by both cost projections and condition projections based on comparison of standard deterioration curves for like asset classes.
Provide the ability to track the asset for financial purposes—book, market, replacement values, cumulative costs, YTD overall cost of ownership (allow for depreciation of the asset using recommended techniques e.g. Straight Line method).
Identify type of asset ownership—example owned, leased, owned but operated by third party.
Track warranty and guarantee information (including responsible purchasing agent, project engineer, vendor or contractor) on the asset ensuring that maintainers are prompted on this type of work.
Provide the ability to display and track (graphically) reliability information on the asset e.g. Mean Time Between Failures.
Compute and track overall equipment efficiency of the asset = Rate x Quality x Efficiency.
Provide standard asset management reports, e.g., in support of O&M GASB 24 and CMOM requirements.

APPENDIX 8.3—SAMPLE KEY TECHNICAL REQUIREMENTS FOR AN ASSET MANAGEMENT SYSTEM

General Requirements
Provide the capability to configure the AMS through Business Rules, Code Tables, and other methods to comply with company's business requirements, without the requirement for customization of the application by coding or other means.
User interface should comply with Microsoft's Windows design guidelines respecting look-and-feel with respect to menus, function keys, online help, tutorials, hyperlinks to the internet etc.
The system should support web-based deployment with scalability to xx number of concurrent users.
Provide the capability to access the AMS using the standard version of Microsoft Internet Explorer 6.0 and beyond.
Support of XML technology, provide integration to Microsoft Office productivity tools using Dynamic Data Exchange (DDE), Object Linking and Embedding (OLE), ODBC, E-mail messaging (MAPI, SMTP).
Support for native TCP/IP network communications.
Ability to support mobile computing for communications over wireless network—view and edit asset records, access work order functions, access inventory and purchasing functions, run queries and reports.
Allow change of terminology used on screens and reports without requiring source code customization.
Provide the ability to attach electronic files (videos, spreadsheets, word documents, photographs, drawings, etc.) to asset related objects throughout the system.
Provide security features for system administration, login and password services, user audit trail (date and time stamp on records changes).
Provide a standard report writing tool and the ability to copy and customize existing system reports.

(continued)

Operating System and Database Requirements
The application server will be running the Microsoft Windows 2000 Server.
The Vendor's solution must run seamlessly on the MS Windows 2000 server and MS Windows XP operating environment (for clients).
System must be capable of operating the database and application on different servers—preferred database is Enterprise Oracle Relational Database Management System (RDBMS) 9i.
Applications should support a normalized database environment and an asset registry.
Provide the ability for data back up and recovery of the database.
Capability to operate the database and application on different servers.
Provide a data dictionary for use by system and database administrators.

Integration Requirements
The AMS must have an open architecture suitable for interfacing and integrating with other systems.
The AMS will be part of Integrated Technology Solution where the following applications will be linked together using the Object Broker integration concept through use of a middleware framework: ERP, EDMS, GIS, CIS, LIMS, SCADA Historian.

CHAPTER 9

Asset Management Standards

Business processes dictate the type of work necessary over the various phases of the asset lifecycle. The organizational aspects of asset management determine how work is coordinated around the asset lifecycle. Asset management standards are the templates that define the plans, procedures, and the deliverables for the business/work processes. Standards are necessary when there are many different groups involved in doing multiple tasks in an environment of continuous change. Standards drive consistency and quality, which are the pillars of asset-related knowledge management. Standards can be either general guidelines or templates that have specific fields to be filled out. Templates filled out for a particular asset are referred to as specifications. Asset management standards can be grouped into the following categories:

- Design standards
- Asset creation standards
- Asset hierarchy
- Asset numbering standards
- Operating standards
- Maintenance standards
- Asset technology standards

There can be unique standards for each of the above areas based on the various asset category and types. The following is an example of asset categories that can be used as a guide.

TABLE 9.1.

Asset Category	Sub Category 1	Sub Category 2	Sub Category 3	Sub Category 4
Linear or Continuous Asset	Pipes	High pressure	Metal	Steel
				Cast Iron
			Plastic	PVC
				ABS
		Low pressure	Concrete	Lined
Linear or Continuous Asset	Electric lines	Transmission	High Voltage	
			Low Voltage	
		Distribution	High Voltage	
			Low Voltage	
Linear or Continuous Asset	Roads	Paved	Freeways	
			City Streets	
		Unpaved		
Linear or Continuous Asset	Land	Commercial		
		Industrial		
		Parks		
Linear or Continuous Asset	Waterways	Lakes		
		Rivers		
		Streams		

(continued)

TABLE 9.1. (continued)

Asset Category	Sub Category 1	Sub Category 2	Sub Category 3	Sub Category 4
Discrete Asset	Plant Equipment	Mechanical	Pumps	Reciprocating Centrifugal Progressive Cavity Diaphragm
Discrete Asset	Compressors	Reciprocating Rotary Turbines		
Discrete Asset	Electrical	Motors	AC DC Variable Speed	
		MCCS Cables		
Discrete Asset	Telecommunications	Telephone	Wired Cellular	
		Microwave Radio		
Discrete Asset	Electronic	Servers PCs Routers Printers		

(continued)

TABLE 9.1. (continued)

Asset Category	Sub Category 1	Sub Category 2	Sub Category 3	Sub Category 4
Discrete Asset	Process Control	Programmable Logic Controllers (PLCs) Actuators Transducers		
Discrete Asset	Buildings	Commercial/Office Residential Industrial		
Virtual	Business Applications	Productivity tools Enterprise Resource Planning Computerized Work Management Systems Process Control Systems		
	Databases Operating systems			

Elements of a Standard—Good Standards Contain the Following Key Attributes or Information

(1) General attributes:
    (a) Name, date last updated and version
    (b) Prepared by—person or group
    (c) Location—file folder etc.
(2) Standard intent or objective
(3) Benefit of using the standard
(4) Summary of standard details
(5) Body—containing the full details
(6) Process for queries or suggestions for updating the standard

MANAGING STANDARDS

For standards to serve their intended purpose, there must be a quality assurance process that ensures the standard is valid. Quality assurance must define the change management process for creating new standards, modifying existing standards and for making standards inactive or deleting them. For this approach to be effective, there must be an owner of the standard who ultimately approves any changes. The owner can be an individual or a working committee or group. The next key requirement is the use of an Electronic Document Management System (EDMS) for enabling the process. This will allow easy storage, access, version control, approvals, and the necessary security features necessary to establish the quality assurance and control process. The following process is recommended for managing standards:

(1) Standard is developed as a draft with an associated display profile in the EDMS.
(2) Draft standard is circulated for review and comments.
(3) Updated standard is sent through the designated approval route.
(4) Standard is approved and set up with appropriate security—access, read, write rights, plus permissions to make a copy or check out the document.
(5) Standard is made active and stored in the EDMS as Version 1.
(6) All potential users of the standard are informed of the existence of the standard, the recommended use through appropriate communication methods (email, memo, face to face meetings etc.) and the process for providing suggestions for updates.

(7) Any suggestions for changes or updates must be documented in a change request form and be sent through the appropriate review/approval route.

(8) On approval the standard is revised and stored as Version 2 in the EDMS.

(9) Communication about the updated standard is then sent to all users.

(10) When a standard becomes obsolete and is no longer in use, it is made inactive in the EDMS and all users are informed of the new status. Standards should only be deleted based on your company's records management guidelines.

APPENDIX 9.1—SAMPLE ASSET MANAGEMENT STANDARDS

Asset Numbering Standard

Asset Numbering Standard	Standard Number: AM0001-05
Version	1.0
Date Created	January 1, 2006
Date last updated	No updates.
Prepared by:	John Smith, Chairman, Assets Standards Committee.
Location:	EDMS Database, File Folder: C:\EDMS\Asset Numbering.
Standard Intent or Objective	Ensure consistency in asset numbering by all business units over the asset lifecycle.
Benefits of using the standard	• Eliminate duplication of asset records (under different asset numbers). • Eliminate possibility of safety issues, e.g., PCS asset number being different from that in the CMWS causing the wrong asset to be locked and tagged for work. • Allow all updates to the asset record (specifications, commissioning data, operating statistics, cost, work history etc.) to be available to all users by accessing one asset number.

Summary of standard details	Asset Numbering Scheme: xxx-xx-xxx-xxxx-xxx
Body—containing the full details	*Facility Site Code:* the site code provides a unique number to identify a specific facility when there are multiple facilities.
	Process or sub-process: helps to identify the various processes or sub-processes in the plant or facility.
	Location or Loop number: this number ensures that the correct asset location or control loop is being referenced for operations or maintenance work. This is important, since an asset may be removed from a location and be replaced by another asset. However, control systems will still control the location.
	Equipment of Instrument Code: the equipment code refers to the specific asset that is being operated or will be worked on. Work at this level will result in both a cost and work history for the asset.
	Suffix for duplicates: the suffix may be used to identify duplicates of the asset or instrument.
Process for queries or suggestions for updating the standard	Queries on use of the standard should be directed to Asset Standards Committee.
	Updates or suggested changes should be documented in an appropriate change request form and sent to the Asset Standards Committee:
	Phone: xxx-xxx-xxxx, or by email to *asc@mycompany.com*

Project Management Standard

Project Management Standard	Standard Number: AM0012-04
Version	2.0
Date Created	November 14, 2005
Date last updated	May 2, 2006
Prepared by:	Dave Brown, Projects Representative, Assets Standards Committee.
Location:	EDMS Database, File Folder: C:\EDMS\Project Management 01
Standard Intent or Objective	Ensure consistency in project delivery and smooth handover of assets to owners.
Benefits of using the standard	• Consistent project delivery practice by all project managers. • Ensures co-ordination by all parties needed to deliver a successful project. • Reliable and consistent high quality project management deliverables.
Summary of standard details	Project Management Check List: Project Details | Approvals | Coordination | Inspections/ Commissioning | Warranty/ Guarantees
Body—containing the full details	*Project Details:* description of the project, activities, resourcing, milestones and deliverables. *Approvals:* the people involved in the approval process for budgets, change orders and key scope items are cited as are decisions made. Co-ordinations: listing and tracking of all groups that need to sign off on milestones and deliverables, attend key meetings and receive key progress reports. *Inspections & Commissioning:* I & C denotes the inspections by internal staff and regulatory federal/state inspectors at stages in the project and a check list of all commissioning events for assets with associated data captured.

(continued)

Body—containing the full de-tails *(continued)*	Warranty/Guarantees: A warranty is a checklist certifying that all of this type of information is captured, entered into the appropriate tracking system (e.g., EAMS) and handed off to the relevant personnel for management.
Process for queries or sugges-tions for updating the stan-dard	Queries on use of the standard should be directed to an Asset Standards Commit-tee. Updates, or suggested changes should be documented in an appropriate change request form and sent to the Asset Stan-dards Committee: Ph: xxx-xxx-xxxx, or by email to *asc@mycompany.com*

CHAPTER 10

Design of an Asset Management Program

At this point in the book, readers should be thoroughly convinced and chomping at the bit to get going with asset management. This chapter discusses the high level design of an AM program. A two-phase approach is recommended for developing a sustainable asset management program—*Phase 1, Design and Phase 2, Implementation and Sustainability*. Phase 1 focuses on taking you and your staff from education on asset management to development of the design appropriate to your industry and company culture. Phase 2 addresses implementing the design solutions, preferably in a pilot environment followed by rollout to the rest of the operations and then developing and sustaining a culture of continuous improvement. The various steps involved in Phase 1 are discussed in detail in this chapter. Phase 2 is discussed in Chapter 12. The fundamental objectives of an asset management program are optimum asset performance, minimal cost of ownership of assets and maximum asset reliability and availability. As we have discussed, optimum performance can only be achieved by pursuing efficiencies in three key business dimensions—assets, people, and processes (see Figure 10.1). Your physical, financial, technological assets should propel your business forward if your people consciously leverage them through well-designed business processes.

Transforming your business to one that has assets, people, and processes properly balanced and working in concert with each other requires commitment and sponsorship at all levels in the organization. The transformation process must be structured and must consider your unique operating environment and company culture.

185

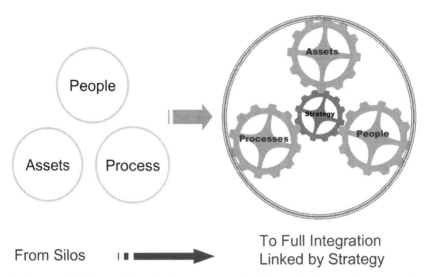

FIGURE 10.1 *Optimal Asset Performance Requires Integration Across Assets, People and Processes.*

OUTSOURCING VERSUS USING IN-HOUSE RESOURCES

Some companies have the expertise in house to successfully design and implement an asset management program. However, most companies are not sure where to start and do not have the necessary resources. In fact, one of the reasons that a company really needs asset management is because they probably lack in-house expertise. Companies have tried unsuccessfully to implement an asset management program using internal resources because of a lack of experience, a lack of resources, and a lack of sponsorship within the organization for the project. Conversely, other companies have spent fortunes on consulting fees to design and implement asset management programs and have many horror stories to tell about the experience. The following diagram Figure 10.2 depicts the "A to Z Implementation Concept." Essentially, the program can be viewed as a continuum, where at one end, a consultant is hired to do everything on behalf of the client, with minimal involvement by client employees. At the other end of the spectrum, the client undertakes the entire program in house with very little external support. Both approaches are fraught with problems. In the first example, using external resources can result in a quick implementation and incorporation of best-in-class practices. Usually, this option is very costly, allows for very little knowledge transfer to in-house staff, and can generate poor system acceptance by users. In the second example, there can be a low-cost project with a high level of buy-in and ownership, but the process usually takes a very long time and the existing business processes are generally duplicated. The obvious solution is a mix of external and internal resources to create a cost-effective solution, to incorporate best-in-class work asset management practices and to maximize knowledge transfer to internal staff needed for continuous improvement and sustainability.

Outside experts should be educators and facilitators helping your staff take control of their destiny and eventual ownership of any solution developed. As a result, your staff can continue to sustain and improve the business operations and at the same time keep consulting to a minimum.

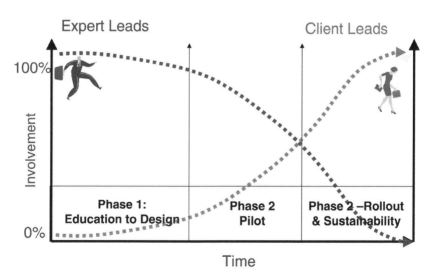

FIGURE 10.2 *Knowledge Transfer is Key to Sustainability of Your AM Program.*

Asset Management Project Team

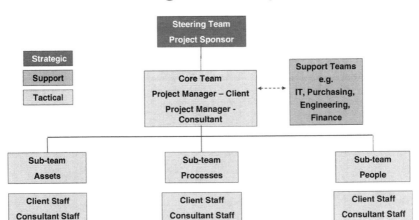

FIGURE 10.3 *Typical Project Team Arrangements.*

PROJECT TEAMING ARRANGEMENTS FOR AN ASSET MANAGEMENT PROGRAM

After the need for an asset management program has been identified and its justification completed, the first task is to develop the project team arrangements to design and implement the program. A standard project team arrangement is based on creating various teams to fill strategic, tactical and support roles. A typical project team is shown in Figure 10.3.

For asset management to have a remote chance of being successful, there must be a strong project sponsor. This person will do the initial groundwork to get asset management moving and also do the preliminary planning for the program. The project sponsor will be instrumental in setting up the steering team to provide overall strategic direction for the program. Because asset management touches all areas of the company's operations, team members should represent: operations, maintenance, materials management, engineering and construction, information technology, finance and planning. If you have decided (based on Figure 10.2) that outside expert help can be beneficial to your program, it may be necessary at this stage to develop a suitable request for proposal and select the best consulting firm to partner with you on this important program. It would be advisable to consider retaining this resource for the entire selection and implementation phases of the project. This means defining the scope of the services required, developing a request for proposal for consulting services, and selecting a suitable candidate. Sometimes it is possible to select a consultant without having to go through a competitive process, if it can be shown that the candidate is uniquely qualified and has good references. Once the consultant is engaged, the first responsibility is to work with the asset management project sponsor to determine the best internal team members to form part of the core team. This group (including the consultant) must have all the skill sets necessary to successfully design and implement the vision for asset management. The team must also have the knowledge required to understand the various phases of the asset lifecycle, the associated business processes and the people arrangements to execute these processes. Like the steering team, team members should represent: operations, maintenance, materials management, engineering and construction, information technology, finance and planning. The start of the design phase is critical for the asset management program and as such selection of team members is a very important step in the process. Similarly, establishing the right internal leadership for the project at this stage is very critical to success. The desired qualifications, experience, roles and responsibility of the team leader are given in Appendix 10.1. The following are the typical resources that can make up the core team—maintenance trade, operator, materials manager, maintenance/project engineer, financial analyst, systems analyst (IT), and planning analyst. A complete list of desired roles and responsibilities, together with qualifications and experience is given in Appendix 10.2. Once the team is established, team members are then provided with background information on the project (business case expected results and high level project plan). They are now ready to embark on the design and implementation of the asset management program as shown in Figure 10.4.

You should not be surprised that you are probably doing asset management in some form already. The above framework serves to help you go through a structured process that will ensure real and sustainable results in the asset management area. There are four steps in Phase 1 the Education to Design phase for asset management:

(1) *Step 1*—Education on asset management best practices concepts and project planning.
(2) *Step 2*—Asset management assessment (or review). Builds a sense of urgency based on the gap analysis and opportunities, business case.
(3) *Step 3*—Strategy and visioning. Seeks to build a guiding coalition,

Asset Management: Design and Implementation Focuses on Assets, People and Processes

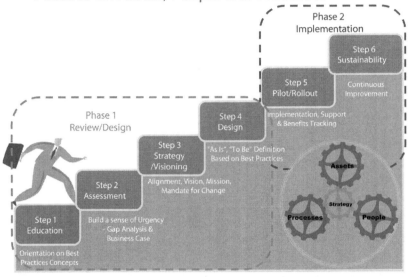

FIGURE 10.4 *Asset Management Program Design and Implementation.*

through alignment , development of a vision and mission for asset management and a mandate for change.

(4) *Step 4*—Detailed design. Documentation of "As Is" asset management practices and development of the "to be" practices, based on best-in-class concepts and an understanding of your unique operating context.

Each of these steps will now be elaborated.

Step 1—Education on Asset Management Best Practices Concepts and Project Planning

This is an essential step to help everyone at all levels in the company understand what is asset management and how it differs from existing practices or how similar it is to existing practices. During this process it is important that the objectives and benefits of asset management are clearly defined. The concepts and ideas discussed in the previous chapters of this book (Chapters 5 and 6) are excellent resources for developing an overview of asset management. It can also be very helpful to mix an interactive simulation to demonstrate how these best practices can make a real difference to the bottom line. Education sessions should target both senior management as well as front line staff. At the end of these sessions all should be aware of the benefits of business transformation as well as the challenges associated with such a change process. Recent examples of companies that have implemented an asset management program and also realized sustained results will lend plausibility to the idea of implementing an asset management program in your company. Deliverables from this step are:

- Education materials on asset management
- Change readiness survey responses
- Project teaming arrangements—steering and core teams and the appropriate mix of external resources
- Relevant team charters
- Detailed project plan for the asset management program
- Alignment from staff on what's involved in asset management as well as the benefits from such a program.

Step 2—Asset Management Assessment (or Review)

Assessment begins with a facilitated exploration of the current state, recognizing the present reality of the business. The three interlocking keys to success: assets (productive and supporting, in particular the enabling technology used and its deployment), people, business processes and their execution are carefully reviewed to identify opportunities facing the organization. Your staff already is aware of the "as is" state through observations, apart from management judgment. Their awareness includes what has led to that state, recognizing the capabilities that were used and developed along the way. This can lead to insight into capabilities and potential, providing the basis from which further expansion can occur. Figure 10.5, represents the review steps:

Answers to the questions in the graphic can be derived based on a desk audit of the operations (review of asset-related documentation, work history and work procedures), site visits, interviews, and the experience of the review staff. The results are documented in a report suitable for widespread dissemination across your organization. It includes opportunities (quantified in a business case) and what it will take to implement them. It provides a perspective for future choices. The deliverables from this step are:

Sample Asset Management Review

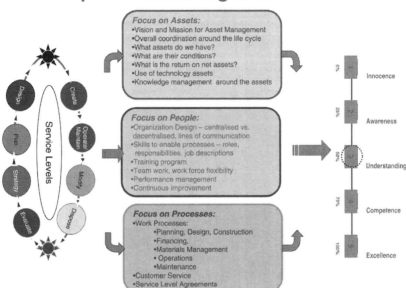

FIGURE 10.5 *Asset Management Review Based on the Asset Lifecycle.*

- Documentation of the review process (findings, conclusions and high-level recommendations)
- Overall rating in the area of asset management on the innocence-to-excellence scale.
- Compelling business case for moving forward with an asset management program to realize the opportunities uncovered.
- Communication pieces necessary for the project team to win management's approval for proceeding with steps 3 and 4 as well as gaining buy–in from other company staff for the program.

Step 3—Strategy and Visioning

This step seeks to build a guiding coalition, through alignment (Figure 10.6), development of a vision and mission for asset management and a mandate for change. This step is critical to having the entire team, which may be all over the map on what asset management is and how can it help, become focused on the common objectives of maximum asset reliability and minimum cost of ownership. This is done through a series of Visioning/Planning workshops with a wide cross-section of staff. Participants are also asked to complete a change readiness survey (sample shown in Appendix 10.1), and these together with the completed surveys from Step 1 are compiled to identify the state of readiness for change in the organization. Change strategies are then developed in a facilitated session with a cross-section of your key people.

The results of this exercise and the two previous workshops will be used to develop a detailed implementation plan with a supporting business case.

Step 4—Detailed design

Detailed design is the step that helps you develop the roadmap to the vision for asset management. It is carried out in a series of workshops that starts with documentation of "As Is" or current asset management practices around the asset lifecycle. A listing and description of these business processes is provided in Chapter 6 together with leading practices in each area. When all parameters of the current state are captured, the desired or 'To Be" business processes are developed by applying best asset management concepts with a focus on new or modified behaviors as per Figure 10.7.

The redesign workshops are interactive and leverage the knowledge of staff and subject matter experts to develop solutions that will give real results in your business environment. An expert facilitator can minimize

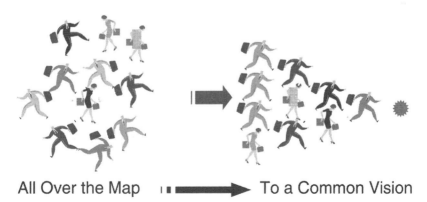

Visioning Step Creates Alignment in Staff

All Over the Map → To a Common Vision

FIGURE 10.6 Alignment on What Asset Management is and Means to the Organization is Critical for Success.

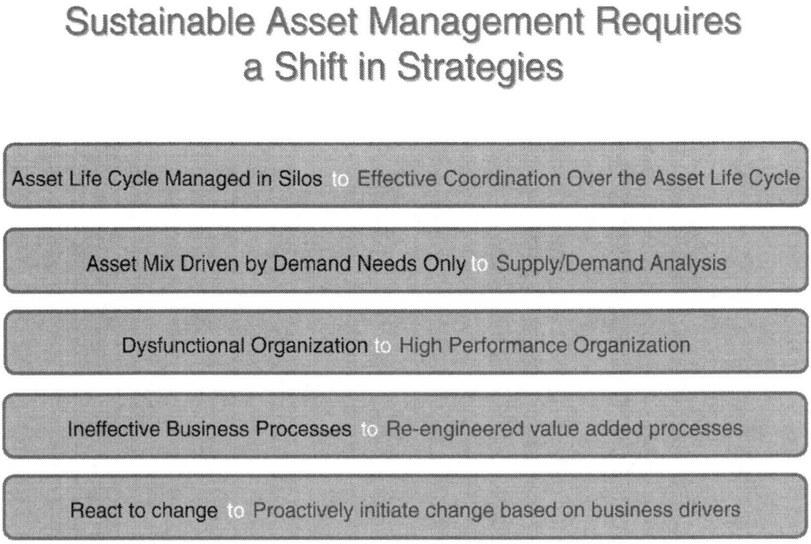

Sustainable Asset Management Requires a Shift in Strategies

Asset Life Cycle Managed in Silos to Effective Coordination Over the Asset Life Cycle

Asset Mix Driven by Demand Needs Only to Supply/Demand Analysis

Dysfunctional Organization to High Performance Organization

Ineffective Business Processes to Re-engineered value added processes

React to change to Proactively initiate change based on business drivers

FIGURE 10.7 *A Shift in Behaviors is Necessary for Sustainable Asset Management.*

the time required to arrive at practical and innovative design solutions. The facilitator can help the redesign team members rise above personal interests, manage conflict constructively, and lead the team to solutions that will help the organization achieve its vision for asset management. The output or deliverables from the redesign step are:

- Workshop notes
- "As Is" process mapping—defining all the steps in the process (electronic, paper- based or verbal), current performance metrics and targets and a listing of all the roles, responsibilities, job descriptions and number of actual people "touching" the process.
- "To Be" process mapping—defining all the steps in the process (all value added—electronic, paper based or verbal), desired performance metrics and targets and a listing of all the roles, responsibilities and the number of people needed to execute the process effectively.
- Design solutions for improved organizational effectiveness across the asset lifecycle —structure, service-level agreements, number of organizational layers and desired spans of control.
- Detailed communication plan that will provide the "grease" to the change process.

- Core recommendations in asset, people, and process areas as well as "quick wins" needed for program viability.
- A Strength, Weakness, Opportunity, and Threat (SWOT) analysis (sample shown in Appendix 10.2) of the design solutions.
- Detailed implementation plan, schedule, resourcing and project teaming arrangements.
- Overall redesign report that clearly summarizes the re-design activities and results.
- Presentation of re-design findings, conclusions and recommendations to your executive management for review and approval to proceed with implementation.

On completion of Phase 1 you and your staff should be fully motivated about realizing the vision everyone has participated in developing in steps 1 to 4. The steps, tasks and activities associated with phase 2 will be discussed in detail in Chapter 12.

Step 5—Implementation

Implementation can be a pilot followed by a full-scale rollout of the designs for assets, people, and business processes. This is the stage where design solutions developed in the re-design workshops are actively piloted. The pilot will be an opportunity to maximize knowledge transfer where learning can be used to adjust the implementation plan for other areas. The knowledge transfer methodology discussed above ensures that your staff are trained up and competent to take the lead in rolling out the various asset, people and process concepts to the other areas of your organization. The pilot is also a valuable opportunity to provide much needed recognition and reward to staff who have made the project successful.

Step 6—Sustainability

The sustainability step focuses on sustaining the gains in asset management and implementing a culture of continuous improvement around the asset lifecycle. This stage of the implementation process focuses on sustaining the results by anchoring the new ways of working into the company's culture. Performance management, decision making driven by high quality data and a culture of continuous improvement ensure that your organization will sustain its reputation as a high-performance business.

APPENDIX 10.1—SAMPLE CHANGE READINESS ASSESSMENT

Topic	Topic	Disagree or Agree (1–10)
1.0 *Leadership*		
1.1	There is a common vision for change	
1.2	Leaders are committed to change	
1.3	There is a strong sense of urgency for change	
1.4	Leaders understand trust and respect each other	
1.5	Leaders are modeling new values and behaviors	
1.6	Leaders are taking the time and effort to win support from other staff	
1.7	We have a history of successful change in this organization	
1.8	Leaders have no other motives that conflict with this change agenda	
1.9	Change will be supported by the current management style and behavior	
	Subtotal	
2.0 *Vision for Change*		
2.1	The rationale for this change is clear and compelling	
2.2	I have a clear understanding of the roadmap to achieve the vision	
2.3	I understand what this change means for me	
2.4	I understand what I need to do to achieve the vision Subtotal 3.0 Change Strategies	
	Subtotal	
3.0 *Change*		
3.1	The current approach to change will work well in this organization	
3.2	There is clear authority and accountability for this change process	
3.3	There is a clear project structure for keeping change on track	

(continued)

Topic	Topic	Disagree or Agree (1–10)
3.4	Problems that emerge will be dealt with effectively in a timely manner	
3.5	There is understanding of the issues involved and sufficient time has been allowed for the change process	
3.6	Related projects will be well coordinated with this change initiative	
3.7	Change progress is usually well monitored and shared with everyone	
3.8	The current organization structure will support this change strategy	
3.9	The existing job descriptions will support this change strategy	
3.10	The change team is working effectively with each other	
	Subtotal	
4.0 *Overcoming Resistance to Change*		
4.1	Employees are encouraged to provide constructive feedback on this initiative	
4.2	Commitment of middle managers is being won before they are expected to lead change	
4.3	Managers have the skills needed to be successful at change management	
4.4	There are rewards and recognition for participating in the imitative and consequences for not doing so	
4.5	There is all way communication on the change initiative—everyone who needs to know is in the know!	
4.6	Everyone who will be impacted is clear on how change affects them and what they need to do differently	
4.7	Employees are encouraged to change rather that being coerced into change	
4.8	This change process is a win-win for everyone (company, clients, employees)	
4.9	Staff expect this change to succeed	

(continued)

Topic	Topic	Disagree or Agree (1–10)
4.10	Staff will be given adequate training to achieve the new skills and behaviors to be successful	
	Subtotal	
5.0 *Managing Staff Performance*		
5.1	Company policies, rules and processes are being changed to support this initiative	
5.2	Change will be supported by current compensation, appraisal and career development processes	
5.3	The desired level of cross functional cooperation is in place for this change to take place	
5.4	Staff will genuinely work to support this change process rather then give the impression that they are supporting change	
5.5	Change will be supported by current skill development processes (training programs etc.)	
	Subtotal	
	Total	

Interpretation of Scores:

High State of Readiness for Change—75 to 100%
Medium State of Readiness for Change—50 to 75%
Low State of Readiness for Change—25 to 50%

APPENDIX 10.2—SAMPLE STRENGTH WEAKNESS OPPORTUNITY AND THREAT (SWOT) ANALYSIS

Strengths	Weaknesses
• Structured and proven methodology to plan, design and execute an Asset Management Program • "Quick wins" can create early successes for the program • Implementation methodology is based on knowledge transfer resulting in ownership and buy-in with staff • Provides a process for keeping the enabling technology asset solution current with changes in the technology area • Sets the stage for a culture of continuous improvement and sustainability	• Existing asset management processes are manual and would require radical re-engineering to become best in class • Could be a challenge to resource the asset management program and at the same time continue to "put out fires" in a reactive work environment • No obvious and/or passionate sponsor for asset management • Lack of buy-in from Corporate IT for the integrated technology asset solution • The benefits of change: "what's in it for me" may not be clearly understood by those who need to change to achieve the vision for asset management
Opportunities	Threats
• Proactively understand and plan for the business drivers that will impact sustainability of the operations • Helps deal effectively with projected funding crises • Can create a culture of corporate knowledge management based on ongoing knowledge capture, refinement and sharing • Meet regulations confidently through reliable and cost effective asset performance	• Very strong and militant union that has traditionally resisted any change projects in the past • Lack of available funding for the program • Customers may be resistant to higher cost of products or services • Inability to free up internal resources to work on the program • Lack of qualified local external asset management experts

REFERENCE

1. *Leading Change,* John P. Kotter, 1996.

CHAPTER 11

Funding Strategies for Asset Management

FUNDING STRATEGIES FOR ASSET MANAGEMENT

This chapter provides insight into ways to fund the implementation of an asset management initiative. The approach to funding depends on a number of factors:

- Type of business—public or private.
- New assets.
- Existing assets—upgrade and modification.
- Existing assets—replacement.

Funding Strategies Based on Type of Business—Public or Private

Private Enterprise

While sustainability and a high-performance organization are goals common to private and public industries, there are fundamental differences in terms of how each funds this vision. In private enterprise, there are usually willing buyers for the goods and services created by the company. Prices are set based on: the cost of developing the service or creating the product, demand and supply, level of competition, applicable taxes, and profit margins stemming from desired shareholder returns. Private enterprise tends to develop good business cases for undertaking new projects and is very clear on the funding necessary to create the right assets and maximize the performance of the asset, in order to achieve the projected returns on net assets. Unlike the public sector, private enterprise has very little support, if its operations or products become too costly to compete in local and global markets.

Poor performance in the asset management area can result in the demise of a company, either through acquisition/merger or bankruptcy. When developing a funding strategy in the private sector for new assets or expansion of the existing asset infrastructure it is critical to understand the full cost of ownership of the asset over its projected life. Full cost of ownership must take into consideration what is required up front to improve operability and maintainability of the asset over its lifespan. Capital budgets must therefore seek to cover this requirement in the design and creation stage of the asset lifecycle. Similarly, funding must be available to cover the appropriate business processes, organizational design and staffing numbers, as well as operation and maintenance. Once these costs are developed, the proposed price for the product or service based on sales projections can be established. It is now possible to seek funding for new assets and the associated program needed to ensure effectiveness of the new assets.

Funding can come from many sources:

- Existing cash reserves or investments (if the company has been fiscally responsible in the past).
- Issue of debt (bonds).
- Issue of new stock.
- Funding from venture capitalist.
- Bank loans.
- Government grants or loans.
- Partnership with other companies who have the funds to invest in the new venture.

There are many financial texts that can provide information on these topics.

Public Enterprise

In the public business environment, usually there is no mandate to make a profit from assets. Tax or ratepayers invest in assets through a government agency, which is expected to be fiscally responsible about managing these assets. The officials are the stewards of billions of dollars worth of assets and are directly responsible for public health and safety. Unfortunately, many agencies have done a poor job of taking care of assets. In some cases they have practically run them into the ground by continuing to be reactive with asset management, as they struggle to deal with ongoing business drivers.

Being effective at managing the public's assets would seem to be an easy task. The agencies do not have to pay corporate taxes; they tend to pay lower salaries than private enterprise; and often they receive preferred pricing on material supplies.

Recently, governments in many developed countries are getting into the act by legislating regulations intended to force public agencies to demonstrate effective asset management. In the United States, the federal government enacted the GASB34 (Government and Accounting Standards Board) regulation, which required most public enterprises to demonstrate that they are maintaining their asset infrastructure in a responsible manner. The financial reporting requirements of GASB34 stipulate that municipalities not only report asset book, market, and replacement values using recommended depreciation techniques. The owner must also demonstrate that the appropriate level of investment is being made in the asset infrastructure to maintain its integrity. The CMOM (Capacity Management, Operations & Maintenance) program is intended to achieve the same goal for the wastewater systems. Similar regulations have been implemented in Canada and elsewhere in the world. In Canada, the Public Services Accounting Board (PSAB) is in the process of developing similar guidelines as GASB 34 that will ensure local government reports on the original cost of their assets and the amortization (original cost less residuals) compared to annual results. The challenges faced by many municipalities are a high asset infrastructure condition deficit and very few funds to restore the asset base to the desired level of integrity. The initial response of these companies has been to investigate funding sources to upgrade, modify or replace assets with a poor condition rating.

Funding can come from many sources:

- Lower service levels and associated costs.
- Increased rates for services.
- Increased property taxes.
- Issuance of debt through bonds.
- Grants and funding from state and federal sources.

Look Internally for Funds Before You Look at Outside Sources

A key aspect of funding for an asset management program is to examine internal procedures and identify opportunities for cost reduction coupled with benefits from improved asset performance and reliability. The previous chapters in this book have demonstrated that you can achieve this level of asset management effectiveness by focusing on assets, people and processes, at the same time as you consider each aspect of the asset lifecycle. Chapter 4 showed how you can develop a business case for asset management by developing the various costs associated with an asset management program as well as the tangible and intangible benefits. Figure 11.1 shows that there is an initial investment and the project can have a negative present value (NPV) for a small time period before the returns make the NPV increasingly positive.

However, the overall NPV for the project can be significant. Even more important is that in addition to the positive financial indicators, there are also changes in behaviors for managing assets. This is key to a culture of continuous improvement and sustainability in your business.

More money to replace or upgrade defective or obsolete assets will buy a temporary reprieve only. In the case of municipal assets, the reprieve may be enough so that the people responsible for taking care of the assets can retire and leave the next generation with the burden. In the case of private enterprise, the timeframe may be much shorter. If the underlying issues that caused the problem in the first place are not addressed then you will be in a similar position in the future. If the goal is to maximize return on the investment, extend useful life, and improve performance and reliability of the asset, it is clear that changes must be made not only to the asset but also to the people and business processes as well. Another important requirement for asset management is integration of activities by different divisions or departments when work is being planned and exe-

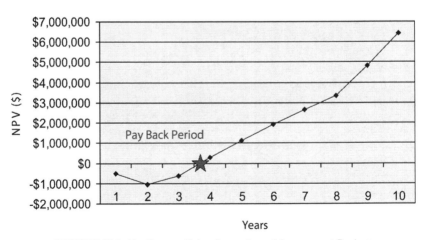

FIGURE 11.1 *Net Present Value for an Asset Management Project.*

cuted on contiguous assets.. For example, it is a very common practice (this is a major issue with many taxpayers), to see the municipality conduct road resurfacing in a street and then a few weeks after see the sewer or electricity people dig up the road again to conduct asset replacement or repairs. If there is adequate planning and integration (absent an emergency) the underground work should be coordinated and done first (water, sewer, gas, telecommunications and electricity), followed by the road resurfacing. This will minimize the cost and inconvenience to the citizen as well as the overall cost of asset ownership. The integrated approach has been gaining prominence as technology solutions make it easier for different groups to access each other's capital programs and weekly work schedules and provide input on integration of work.

Developing the Capital Programs

Capital programs represent a more substantial use of company funds compared to operating budgets. It is no wonder that sustainable asset management must place a considerable focus on this area. A well-planned capital program can mean the difference between excellence and mediocre performance.

Capital program for new assets—A capital program for new assets can be linked directly to the company's strategic planning process for growth and profitability. These strategies can translate into new plants, expansion of existing facilities, acquisition of companies etc. The decision to add new assets must be made based only on good supply and demand analysis, together with an appropriate risk assessment for each project. All the tactical items or projects should be supported by sound business cases based on the lowest overall cost of ownership of the asset. The business case will be the basis for securing funding for the project, phasing of expenditure during implementation, and benefits tracking over the life of the project. In planning capital projects, it is important to estimate the extent of use of internal resources as well as outside contracting or consultant resources. The cost of the impact on the operations and any steps to minimize this impact must also be considered in the business case. Too often projects are planned without adequate accounting for the use of O&M staff. This ends up being charged to operating budgets, which are then deprived of resources.

Capital program for existing assets—Development of a capital program can be haphazard, compared to the program for new assets. Capital programs tend to be very reactive in nature and usually without proper justification or business cases. It is not surprising to hear managers complain they were unable to get funding to upgrade, modify or replace poor performing assets. Here are several tips for developing a successful capital program:

- Ensure that all assets are properly set up in the CWMS with all ongoing work and cost history updated on a regular basis.
- Ensure that an adequate condition rating system is in place for the various asset categories and regular audits are done.
- Analyze the above data to identify candidates for upgrades, modifications, and replacement, and develop sound business cases to support the individual projects.
- Seek management's support and approval for the capital program.
- Execute the capital program by teaming with the relevant experts (internal engineering and construction staff, consultants and contractors) ensuring that the projects are delivered on time, within scope, budget and the impact on the operations is well managed
- Ensure that the Capital Projects workflow is re-engineered to have only value added steps and leverages technology tools to manage projects more effectively.
- Conduct ongoing benefits tracking for projects and leverage this to clearly demonstrate that investment in the existing asset infrastructure can also yield significant returns on investment.

Phasing of Expenditure

Financial efficiency requires the financial department in the company to be able to manage the company's cash flow in a manner that ensures the viability of the operations. This entails re-investing excess funds in the company (both long and short term instruments), securing the best loans (again short- and long-term), and ensuring that cash is available to fund the company's operations. Poor planning for capital projects can create financial crises, resulting in a need for emergency funding or funds being allocated and not used as planned, where these could have been invested in other deserving projects. The results are missed opportunities and scarce funds. Even if there is good planning in projects on new or existing assets, a company can easily experience peaks in demand for capital financing, when there are not many projects. Figure 11.2 provides a typical financial expenditure projection for a capital program in the municipal sector. Some practitioners in the asset management field refer to this projection as the "Nessie Curve." These peaks and valleys can create stress and inefficiency in the financial system. Good asset management practices help smooth out the curve and expedite the secur-

Phasing of Expenditure for Capital Projects

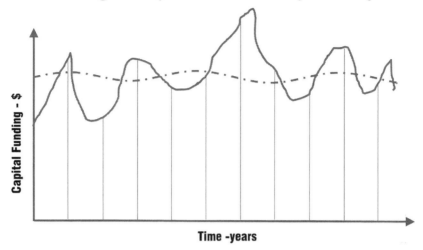

FIGURE 11.2 *Typical Capital Program Phasing of Expenditure.*

ing and use of funds. In fact, when an asset management program is successfully implemented, the curve is not only smoother and more predictable but also lower as a result of lower ownership costs of the asset mix.

Funding an asset management program requires a strong partnership among planners, engineers (design and construction), finance officers, and operations/maintenance personnel. A properly funded program will transform the annual budget grind into a proactive method of ongoing management of the asset mix, to ensure that the company owns the right assets and can operate and maintain them effectively. The capital and operating budgets is a natural by-product of this proactive method of managing assets.

REFERENCES

1. *Government Accounting and Standards Board (GASB) website: www.gasb.org.*
2. *Chartered Accountants of Canada website: www.cica.ca.*

CHAPTER 12

Implementing an Asset Management Program

IMPLEMENTING AN ASSET MANAGEMENT PROGRAM

Program implementation is where the "rubber hits the road" and must be properly executed in order to realize the benefits of the program. This chapter provides detailed information on phase two of an Asset Management Program. This takes us through Steps 5 (*Pilot and Rollout to all remaining areas*) and Step 6 (anchoring new behaviors in the company's culture to achieve Sustainability) in the implementation process shown in Figure 12.1.

Implementation Strategy

There are two major approaches to implementation: (1) Big bang—rollout to all sites at the same time and (2) a pilot followed by rollout to all sites. This is a strategic decision you must make prior to embarking on implementation. Here are some key points to guide you in making this decision:

Big Bang Approach

Many companies have decided because of resource concerns and timing issues to "bite the bullet" and implement the design solutions in all areas at once. This approach can reduce the overall implementation schedule and minimize the pain associated with radical change. It also provides an avenue for different departments that are anxious and eager to implement the program to start moving forward. The Big Bang ap-

Asset Management: Design and Implementation Focuses on Assets, People and Processes

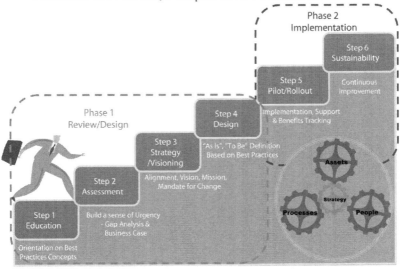

FIGURE 12.1 *Asset Management Design and Implementation.*

proach does have its setbacks. It requires a high level of coordination. Also, there is a peak demand for resources. Often it is more difficult to manage the change process all at once. Finally if there are glitches in the design solutions, the entire company may be affected by these issues as the implementation team tries to resolve them. The latter problem can dilute interest and reduce enthusiasm for the program.

Pilot Followed by Rollout to All Areas

A pilot followed by rollout allows the implementation team more time to plan, coordinate, and execute the delivery process. By focusing on a pilot area, the team can test the design solutions and make adjustments at the same time confining problems to smaller groups. The team can also learn as much as possible about implementation and in this way limit the use of external consultants in the subsequent rollout process. The learnings from the pilot go a long way in detailed rollout planning and change management. The pilot followed by rollout method can also result in quick triumphs for the program, which may be necessary to win approval for full-scale implementation. There are, however, challenges with this approach. It can take longer and can frustrate early adopters, who are not in the pilot and yet are eager to implement the solutions in their areas.

I have found that the latter approach tends to yield better and more sustainable results. The approach based on a pilot followed by full rollout of business design to all operations in the company will be explained in more detail.

Selection of the AM implementation team

The Steering Team for the program should continue to have the same membership to provide oversight and guidance for Phase 2. You should consider modifying the Core Team at this stage of implementation. It may be a good idea to check in with Core Team members to see if they are prepared to see the entire program through or if they would like to do other things. In addition, you may want to replace certain members with others more experienced in front line activities. Once the teaming arrangements have been finalized for Phase 2, there are three preliminary steps before actual implementation can start—*development of the communication plan, the implementation road map, and the project's work breakdown structures (WBS).*

The Communication Plan

A communication framework may have been developed in Phase 1. If so, it is necessary only to update the plan to include the communications requirements for implementation. If a framework was not developed, then this is a unique opportunity to prepare the user community. The various audiences, key messages, the medium for communication, who delivers the message, and when (how often) should be determined. Effective communication will help alleviate apprehension about what will be happening during implementation, set the right expectations, and pave the way for support. In general, one communication plan can be developed for both Phase 1 and Phase 2. A template for developing a communications plan is given in Appendix 12.1.

The Implementation Road Map

Many people struggle to understand or visualize what is expected of them during implementation. The implementation road map is a concept that helps fill this void. In the case of an Asset Management program, the road map paints a picture from the current state to the vision for asset management in terms of desired behaviors and results (both quantitative and qualitative). The road map should provide this perspective for all the groups affected by the implementation..

In a typical asset management program (of four-year duration) where all the players around the lifecycle are involved, the road map has to be developed for the following groups for each year:

- *Planning*—here the work processes and behaviors of the various teams associated with the evaluation, strategy and planning activities are detailed for each year.
- *Finance*—desired behaviors of all teams associated with funding new assets, operating and maintaining existing assets, modifying or upgrading existing assets or participating in analyses for replacing or decommissioning of existing assets are mapped.
- *Human Resources*—desired behaviors of human resources staff, partnering with other groups to ensure that the most appropriate people arrangements are in place to get the best assets for the organization and to maximize the returns from these assets.
- *Information Technology*—focuses on behaviors associated with implementation and modeling of the System Development Lifecycle approach to create and manage the integrated

Implementation Road Map – Desired Behaviors and Results

"Road Map": must focus on three main areas:
- – Current State Definition
- – Vision
- – Implementation Plan

FIGURE 12.2 Implementation Road Map.

technology asset solution needed to enable the various work processes around the asset lifecycle.

- *Materials Management*—desired behaviors with respect to procurement of new assets, goods and services and the stocking of necessary spares and operational supplies needed for O&M to maximize the return from the asset mix.
- *Operations*—desired behaviors in operational staff as they learn and practice the revised operational business processes, use technology assets, apply the most effective people arrangements (partnering with all groups as necessary) and use data to drive continuous improvement initiatives.
- *Maintenance*—desired behaviors necessary to partner with all groups to commission new assets, maintain existing assets, maximize reliability and performance and use data to drive asset replacement and continuous improvement initiatives.

As the road map is developed, it may be necessary to drill down to desired behaviors by different teams within a specific group, e.g., engineering and construction may have project design engineers and construction engineers, and the desired behaviors from these groups may differ. Similarly, a plant management team may be required to demonstrate different behaviors from front line teams. In addition, certain groups may already be demonstrating the desired behaviors, well within the four-year project life. The road map, when it is completed, can be used as a checklist or validation tool by the Steering and Core Teams. Similarly, operational staff in the various departments can also use the road map to validate that they are doing what is required of them. The road map is also an excellent communication tool for making the change management process easier.

PROJECT'S WORK BREAKDOWN STRUCTURES (WBS) AND DELIVERABLES

In doing the detailed planning for implementation, a clear picture of the various activities (tasks and sub-tasks), together with associated details such as milestones, level of effort, and deliverables, must be developed. This then drives the project schedule and allows for the identification of the critical path for the project using Critical Path analysis. The following discussion provides an overview of the suggested activities for implementation:

4.1 *Project Management*—project management, a work breakdown structure, may seem simple but can be considered to be the glue that holds the project together. The standard project lifecycle should be followed, together with the best practices associated with each phase. The project phases that must be managed are: *Initiation, Planning, Controlling, Executing, and Closing*[1]. There are many good project management concepts that will help you see your project through to completion. Effective project management ensures that: the project scope is executed as per specifications, within the desired time frames and budgets, and without disruption of operations. The major activities in project management (over each phase of the project lifecycle) are:

4.1.1 *Administration*—focuses on the paperwork to keep the project on track. This includes: regular status reports, tracking of all project documentation, invoices and payments, closeout of key work breakdown structures, and orientation of new project team members.

4.1.2 *Coordination*—comprises the logistics necessary to keep the project moving (e.g., setting up meetings, inviting and confirming attendance of participants, agendas, securing venues, scheduling and sequencing of tasks and sub-tasks). A key part of coordination is effective management of issues and conflicts, as they arise during implementation. This will require an issues log to capture, manage, and track all issues ensuring that the process is one that forces resolution at the most appropriate level, before it is pushed up to higher authorities for resolution.

4.1.3 *Integration of Tracks*—ensures that the best solutions are obtained for the project by careful integration of the design solutions for each track. We have seen in previous chapters that the full benefits from asset management can be achieved only by implementing best-in-class assets, people, and processes. The various solutions in these areas are dependent on each other. For example, you cannot develop or revise business practices unless you are clear on the asset strategy and proposed mix. Similarly, you cannot develop desired people arrangements (organization structure, roles, responsibilities, skill sets, competencies, job descriptions) unless you have nailed down the "to be" business processes.[7]

4.2 Step 5—Pilot

As discussed, the pilot is a great opportunity to manage risk in the implementation process. A pilot is not a field trial, where fail-

---

[7]Project Management Book of Knowledge (PMBOK), 2000 Edition,—by the Project Management Institute Inc.

ure could end the program. The pilot offers an opportunity to test and refine the design solution in an environment where there is a commitment to implement the solution throughout the operations. The following describes the steps in a typical pilot:

4.2.1 *Pilot Selection*—Choosing the right site to pilot the solution is important. Selecting the pilot site is based on the following criteria. The site should be able to demonstrate results. It also contains an existing core of staff who have bought in to the program's ideas, and where the site manager is keen and passionate about asset management. The site should have the necessary infrastructure (e.g. computer hardware and networking), and the scope of implementation on the site should be manageable.

4.2.2 *Detailed planning*—Project management principles are applied to develop the plan ensuring that every detail is defined and documented. The pilot staff should be included in this process to ensure that the operating context and site culture are considered in the plan. The implementation road map developed above and the communication plan should now be customized to make each unique to the pilot area. All pilot staff should be briefed on roles, responsibilities, expected behaviors, and results from the program as it applies to their work environment.

4.2.3 *Implementing Assets, People, and Process elements*—the specific design elements are developed and operationalized in the pilot area. For example:

4.2.3.1 *Assets*—An asset condition audit may be initiated with a view to developing a capital improvement program to get all assets up to a desired level of integrity (95%). The capital projects process can be redesigned to ensure involvement of all groups and to eliminate non-value-added steps. Asset management standards in the areas of asset design, construction, and commissioning can be developed or revised, if they exist.

4.2.3.2 *Processes*—Redesign of all business processes around the asset lifecycle—materials management, operations, maintenance etc. This should yield all workflow steps, enabling technologies, roles, responsibilities, performance metrics and targets, and service-level agreements necessary to manage the assets in the pilot area.

4.2.3.3 *People*—Development of revised organization structures, new or revised job descriptions, skills/competencies, training program, staffing numbers, performance management framework, facilitation of desired team behaviors etc.

The above solutions are examples for discussion purposes. The actual solutions will be based on the design solutions developed in Phase 1 of the program.

4.2.4 *Pilot support and review*—Knowledge transfer, discussed in Chapter 10, where you leverage the knowledge of a consultant or expert to help your staff become self-sufficient, should be applied to the pilot staff. Your implementation team will then be geared to provide on-site coaching, mentoring, and facilitating of conflict resolution to keep the pilot moving. This process will instill confidence in the pilot staff that they can make the new designs part of the normal way of working. Concurrent with this "weaning" activity, the implementation team should be actively reviewing the pilot's progress in all areas, to identify what solutions have worked well and those that are not creating the desired results. The team should modify the latter by collaborating with the pilot staff to make changes that can fit into their operating context. These changes should also be considered for detailed design in the rollout to other areas of the operation.

4.2.5 *Benefits tracking*—As with any project that got the green light based on a convincing business case, it is important to demonstrate that the results are being achieved. The business case should be converted into a benefits tracking document that will track quantitative benefits (compared to the associated investment cost). The implementation road map for the pilot will document the results in the qualitative area (e.g., better teamwork, workforce flexibility, and coordination around the asset lifecycle).

4.2.6 *Rollout planning*—During pilot support and review, high-level planning for rollout to other areas should be in progress. It should consider incorporation of learnings from the pilot to update design solutions, the project integration approach, the project timeline and resourcing, the implementation road map, and the communication plan. It may be necessary to develop revised project team arrangements to include affected staff from other areas. In addition, it is always a good idea to have staff from other sites visit and see for themselves how the program has been implemented and talk to pilot staff about results and changed behaviors. The high-level plan sets the stage for Rollout to all areas.

4.3 Step 5—Rollout

Rollout of the Asset Management program to all areas is similar to the pilot approach except that it is a much larger effort involving more implementation resources and more people affected by change. It entails:

4.3.1 *Detailed planning*—The high level plan developed in at the end of the pilot is elaborated for implementation at the other sites. The plan should include: key milestones, deliverables, and project resources (both project team and site staff). It would also require an update of the overall roadmap and customized roadmaps for each site together with an updated communications framework for the program.

4.3.2 *Implementing Asset, People and Process elements elements*—The updated design solutions are implemented for each of the key business elements.

4.3.3 *Support and review*—Support for a large implementation is always a challenge. It may be possible to enlist some of the pilot staff to help with this important exercise. You have to strike the right balance on implementation schedule and available resources. There should be an ongoing review process to identify and manage issues as early as possible. In addition, you should encourage project team members and staff to celebrate successes—which will help the change process to gain even more momentum.

4.3.4 *Benefits tracking*—The benefits tracking concept discussed at the pilot level is now expanded to the whole program. Both quantitative and qualitative data should be captured and reported on a monthly basis at project status meetings. These results should be made public through the communications framework.

4.4 Step 6—Sustainability

4.4.1 *Continuous improvement (CI) training*—To sustain a high level of performance of your assets and a high level of people effectiveness, you must ensure that the organization develops a culture of continuous improvement. The entire approach so far can be expected to open up avenues for creativity and innovation in staff and will lead to people question the status quo regularly. There will be, hopefully, a plethora of data that can be used to drive decision making about how assets are managed. It is, however, necessary to implement a more formal approach to continuous improvement.

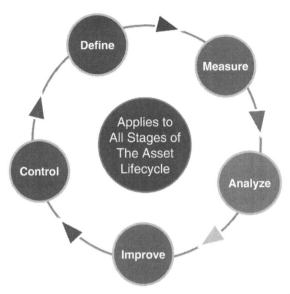

FIGURE 12.3 *Continuous Improvement Sets the Stage for Sustainability.*

Figure 12.2 provides a frame work for continuous improvement and can be implemented in all areas of the operations. It would require specific training for staff, identification of initiatives based on relevant asset data (work, cost history), and use of outside help (if not available internally) to facilitate a CI project. The steps in the process are described below.

- *Define* the critical issues, and core business process involved in the initiative.
- *Measure* the performance of the Core Business Process involved in the initiative.
- *Analyze* the data, determine root causes of problems, and identify improvement opportunities.
- *Improve* business process by designing innovative and practical solutions to fix/prevent problems.
- *Control* the business process by implementing solutions to fix problems and manage performance (closing the CI loop).

Sustainability has an internal focus and an external focus. The internal focus requires active management of performance at all levels in the organization. It also requires a well-developed integrated technology solution to capture, store and make accessible all the data needed to manage assets. The data must support the various performance metrics in your business unit and team-level performance scorecards. The balanced score approach to performance management with measures specific to asset management will be discussed in detail in Chapter 13. The external focus ensures ongoing scanning of the business environment to validate that existing business drivers are real and continue to be a threat to your organization and also identify new and emerging drivers for change.

As part of the ongoing implementation of the asset management program, there should be appropriate recognition and rewards for the project team and participating staff for their efforts at making sustainable asset management a reality in your organization. This can be simply recognition at tailgate meetings, exposure in the company newsletter, or career advancement opportunities. Team recognition and rewards can be mementos (caps, shirts), group outings (golf day), or attendance at conferences to showcase your project to the wider community.

APPENDIX 12.1—TEMPLATE FOR A COMMUNICATION PLAN

Audience (Who) (Examples provided)	Messages (What)	Interest of Audience (Why)	When	How/Deliverable	How Often/Who
Employees	Overall Vision for the Asset Management Program and how it will achieve and sustain best-in-class operations.	Staff needs to know how their work will be impacted by the Am Program	Ongoing during life of project. Specifically at key milestones	Tailgates, possible reports or newsletter for project.	At key milestones and at least a monthly communication
Union	Overall Vision for the Asset Management Program and how it will affect and improve their membership's work process and environment	The union needs to be aware of any potential changes that can affect negotiated items	Ongoing during life of project. Specifically at key milestones	Tailgates, possible reports or newsletter for project.	At key milestones and at least a monthly communication
Project Manager	Frequent project progress (time, scope, money), resource availability etc.	Responsible for successful delivery AM Program, content for newsletter	Throughout the project, start to finish (at key milestones in both projects)	Project management meetings, email, phone, presentation materials	Monthly progress meetings with project manager, planned sessions with other stakeholders
Project Sponsor	Major project milestones, major hurdles	Projected project timelines, implications for staff, licensing issues, cost/benefit analysis	Every month	Regular project management team meetings	Every month (AM Core Team Leader and Consulting PM) Milestone based

(continued)

Audience (Who) (Examples provided)	Messages (What)	Interest of Audience (Why)	When	How/Deliverable	How Often/Who
Management Staff					
Executive Manager					
Other Departments					
Board of Directors					
Customers					

CHAPTER 13

Managing Performance of an Asset Management Program

WHAT IS PERFORMANCE MANAGEMENT?

Performance management was introduced in Chapter 6 as a leading practice for ensuring the sustainability of organizations. Performance management drives behavior. At the same time, performance can be measured. If we measure asset reliability, for example, we will make the necessary decisions to keep maximizing this important parameter. The best strategic plans and intentions can amount to very little unless there are clear goals, objectives, and associated targets to ensure that strategies for success are being achieved. Setting realistic targets and managing performance and expectations around these targets are essentially the practice of performance management. The balanced scorecard approach (Figure 13.1) is a robust framework for performance management and is the most popular method used for managing performance today.

Performance management is closely associated with strategic planning. The following are the main links to the strategic planning process:

- During the visioning step, a corporate scorecard is developed for the various strategies critical to the success of the company.
- The corporate scorecard is then distilled further with the input of a wide cross-section of staff at the business unit level to create the business-unit-level scorecard.
- Further refinement to the frontline team level results in simple team scorecards that are tied directly to corporate goals and objectives.
- Monitoring, trending, feedback and adjustments to plans support your vision of sustainability.

Performance Management Using the Balanced Scorecard Approach

FIGURE 13.1 *Performance Management Using the Balanced Scorecard.*

In the balanced scorecard framework, performance is managed in four areas: customers, financials, people, and processes. In each of these we should be able to identify asset management performance indicators that make sense for a particular business environment. Here are simple questions that can help you determine the relevant metrics for each area.

- *Customers*—How do we want our external customers to see us in the areas of quality, cost, responsiveness, social and environmental?
- *Financial*—What is the overall return on all assets employed in the production of goods or services? How must we appear to our shareholders or the public if we are succeeding financially?

- *People*—Are our people learning and growing with us, are we developing the agility and flexibility necessary to change and continuously improve?
- *Processes*—To satisfy customers, at what processes should we excel, and how do we know that we are excelling at these processes?

The answers to the above questions vary (but are connected) as we move up the organizational chart from the task, operational, tactical, strategic and visioning levels. It is therefore important that all scorecards are connected to the overall company's goals and objectives. Figure 13.2 shows typical scorecards for any organization.

In developing performance scorecards at the various levels, relevant asset management metrics must be included. An effective asset management practice ensures optimal performance by focusing on:

- Making the most appropriate design choices for creating a new asset based on the full cost of ownership, funding strategies, operations and maintenance needs.

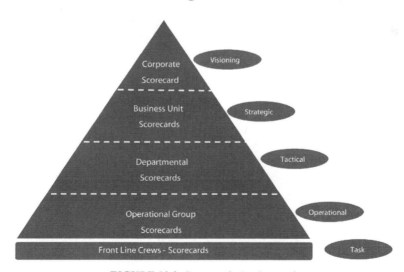

Balanced Scorecard – at all Levels in the Organization

FIGURE 13.2 *Scorecards Are Layered.*

- Involvement of O&M staff in the construction and ownership phase to maximize knowledge transfer.
- Asset preservation through continuously striving to maximize asset reliability and at the same time meet performance standards in a cost-effective manner using the right mix of maintenance philosophies.
- Asset upgrade, modification, and/or replace assets based on sound economic criteria.
- Asset decommissioning or disposal in a manner that maximizes salvage value and at the same time remains mindful of environmental concerns.

A good asset management program should provide measures for the various categories of assets and for the various types of scorecards in the following areas:

(1) Asset Financial Indicators:
- Return On Net Asset (RONA): this is a comparison of the profit earned to the net value (Book Value) of the company assets
- Book, market values, and replacement values[8]
  —*Book value*—literally the value of the company's assets as listed in its accounts; this would be the value after depreciation
  —*Market value*—the value that the company can receive for the assets if it is possible to sell them (or the valuation offered by another firm interested in acquiring the company's assets)
  —*Replacement value*—the cost the company would incur if it had to replace the assets to maintain the service or continue manufacturing products
- Capital Investment:
  —New Assets Capital Program = Total Cost of Capital Program for New Assets/Total Company Budget for the Fiscal Year
  —Upgrades/Modifications = Total Cost of Capital Program For Upgrades and Modifications/Total Company Budget for the Fiscal Year
- Average Asset Age (by Asset Category)—Total Asset Age for

---

[8]Balanced Scorecard, Translating Strategy Into Action, by Kaplan and Norton, Harvard Business Press, 1996.

all Assets in Category / Total Number of All Assets in Category[9]

- Asset Condition Deficit = Total Projected Cost to Bring Assets Back to Desired Condition Integrity/Net Replacement Value of the Company Assets

(2) Asset Performance Indicators

- Overall Equipment Efficiency (>85%) = Quality x Performance Efficiency × Availability

  where:

  —Quality = (Total Production less Defective Product)/Total Production (>99%)

  —Performance Efficiency = (Actual Output for Scheduled Time)/Design Output for Scheduled Time) (95%)

  —Availability = (Scheduled Time minus Down Time)/Scheduled Time (>90%)

- Condition rating index

  —Scale from 1–5 where 1 represents extremely bad condition and 5 represents a "like new" condition.

- Reliability indicators

  —Reliability Index = (Σ Time between failure incidents over a specified time period)/(The number of failures in that time interval)

  —Mean time between failures (MTBF) = Number of Asset Breakdowns/Total Hours in the Time Period

- Management of Work Done on the Assets:

  —% Reactive work = Number of Hours of Reactive Work Orders/Total Work Hours

  —% Proactive Work = Number of Hours of Proactive Work Orders/Total Work Hours

  —% PM Compliance = Total Completed PM hours / Total PM Hours for Scheduled Time Period

  —% Schedule Compliance = Completed Hours in Schedule Period / Total Scheduled Hours for Period

  —% Predictive Maintenance = Total Hours of Completed Predictive PMs / Total PM hours Completed for Period

---

[9]Developing performance Indicators for Managing Maintenance by Terry Wireman, Industrial Press, 1998.

—Work Order Backlog (can be categorized by trade) = Total Hours of Work for Active Work Orders

—Work Request Backlog = Total Number of Work Requests (not converted to Active Work Orders)

—Wrench on Bolt Time = Time Spent Doing Actual Work on Asset/Total Time Associated with the Work Order

—Stores Service Level = Total Number of Orders Filled On Demand /Total Number of Orders Requested

—Inventory Turns = Total Annual Cost of Stores Items Used/Total Inventory Valuation

—Reactive Purchasing = Total Number of Rush Purchase Orders/Total Number of Purchase Orders

- Aesthetics rating (suitable for buildings and overall look of plant and equipment):

  —Scale from 1–5 where 1 represents extremely bad appearance (degraded paint work, corrosion etc.) and 5 represents a "like new" condition

- Technological obsolescence index:

  —Scale of 1–5 where 1 represents obsolescence (no longer supported and a technologically superior asset is available) and 5 represents the latest in technology in the particular field

(3) Safety and the Environment

- Environment:

  —No. of environmental regulatory violations per year

  —Total cost of environmental clean- up and fines due to violations

- Safety:

  —Number of safety violations per year

  —Number of documented near misses

  —Total hours without any lost time accidents

  —Safety work order backlog (number of work orders)

(4) Asset Capital Project Measures:

- Budgeting Effectiveness = Actual Cost of Completed Project/ Original Budget Cost

- Project management measures reflecting:

  —Time—Elapsed Project Time/Total Project Timeline

  —Scope—Completed activities, milestones and deliverables

  —Money (% of Budget) = Actual Expenditure/Budget For Time Period

  —Earned Value—Cost of Actual Work Accomplished/Cost of Planned Work for the Period

- No. of failures during warranty period after commissioning
- No. of incidents of design flaws or oversights identified after commissioning

(5) People Effectiveness:
  - Internal Customer Satisfaction Index—level of satisfaction with service provided on a scale of 1 to 5 where 1 is poor service and 5 is complete satisfaction
  - Maintenance Wrench on Bolt Time = Time spent doing actual work on Asset/Total Time Associated with the Work Order
  - Operator Wrench on Bolt Time = Time spent doing actual work operating or maintaining Assets/Total Available Operations Time
  - Operator Workforce flexibility = Total Hrs. of Work Done on Maintenance Tasks/Total Maintenance Work Hrs.
  - Maintenance Workforce Flexibility = Total Hrs. of Work Done on Operational Tasks/Total Operations Work Hrs.
  - Overtime = Total overtime hours/total available work hours (normal working schedule)
  - Number of union grievances raised during the year
  - Training = Total hours of training taken/Total available work hours in the normal working schedule
  - Production Target Compliance = Actual production/Projected (budgeted) production

(6) Sustainability:
  - Asset Improvement/renewal = Budget dollars spent on asset improvement and renewal/Total Annual O&M Budget
  - Continuous Improvement (CI) Activities:
    —Time spent on CI Initiatives/Total Time Available for Workforce
    —Number of CI projects/Total Projects Done in Department
  - Corporate Knowledge Retention:
    —% of company knowledge that is stored electronically
    —% of staff who feel they have electronic access to the knowledge they need to do their jobs effectively
    —% of staff who actively use electronic data for decision making
  - Succession Planning = Number of positions that have an identified internal successor/Total number of positions
  - Labor turnover = Number of employees leaving the company during the year/Total Number of employees at end of fiscal year

CHAPTER 14

Future Trends That Will Impact Asset Management

THE FUTURE OF ASSET MANAGEMENT

Scientists, engineers, and software programmers are continuously pushing the envelope in the design area to improve asset efficiency, performance, and reliability. Asset design is more sophisticated and concentrated on the lowest overall cost of ownership. Similarly, organization experts are developing concepts that will help companies better manage change, improve the use of people resources, and ensure sustainability of the organization. It is important that the company's staff be proactive in knowing what the new ideas and concepts are and plan at both the vision and strategic level to adopt them. This chapter provides insights into future trends in asset management.

(1) *Design considerations*

    (a) *Computer Aided Engineering (CAE)*—There will be a major shift in design work to computer aided engineering, where designs can be developed and tested in limitless configurations without prototypes being built. CAE will make it possible to evaluate operational and maintainability aspects by computer simulation before investment in physical assets. Car companies have already started using this technology with great success in terms of time to market, reduced costs, and better asset reliability.

    (b) *Energy efficiency*—The unending push for energy savings will continue to drive the development of high-efficiency electric motors, engines, and hybrid drive systems. This will also be a direct result of the asset management objective of lowest cost of asset ownership.

(c) *Automation*—The desire to minimize human interaction in operating and maintaining assets will continue to drive innovative automation of individual assets and processes.

(d) *Robotics*—The concept of robots replacing humans for operating assets will eventually move to the maintenance of assets, especially those in harsh and unsafe environments.

(e) *Smart control systems*—We will see most high-cost and critical assets being equipped with CPUs that allow them to track their overall "health" and also perform self-diagnostics. In this way, the assets can continuously track and trend relevant data. A mini-version of the CWMS can reside on the asset's CPU and will facilitate the basic work management process. In the event of major deviations from targets or set points the asset will:

  (i) Initiate corrective action if the problem is due to changes in operating parameters, or initiate a work request for operations attention.

  (ii) Initiate a suitable work request if the problem is one that needs maintenance attention.

  (iii) In the future, a worker assigned to take care of a particular group of assets will enter a building or work area, and all assets will communicate wirelessly with the worker's PDA and download needed work or information. When work is completed, all data entered by the worker will be immediately uploaded to the asset's CPU and update its database (at the same time resetting parameters, e.g., PMs). This database in turn will be part of an overall network of databases tied to the main CWMS servers.

(f) *Modularization*—Modular components will be used to save repair time. In addition to extended Mean Time Between Failures (MTBF), there will be vast improvements in Mean Time To Repair (MTTR).

(g) *Safety*—Asset design, operation and maintenance will continue to focus on eliminating hazards, improving accessibility for people to work safely around assets, and leverage automation and control to protect both the asset and people from catastrophic failure.

(h) *Environment*—Increasing concern about the environment will drive technological advances and asset design innovations to minimize air, water, soil and noise pollution. We can expect legislators to reinforce this behavior through more stringent regulations.

(i) Security concerns—Terrorism and asset destruction have made it very clear to everyone that asset design must include securing the asset against terrorism and sabotage. Vulnerability assessments should be carried out at the design stage. Design components that will deter and/or prevent attacks for critical asset infrastructure must be incorporated. Your company should conduct a vulnerability assessment of all current asset infrastructure, and implement changes to protect your investment and people resources.

(2) *A Transition from Mechanical to Electrical Engineering*—Traditionally, electrical engineers move the light stuff, e.g., electrons, power, bits and logic, while mechanical engineers do the heavy lifting, e.g., moving the atoms and molecules. Electricity travels close to the speed of light, whereas mechanical systems move at the speed of sound or slower. There will be a clear trend to using electrical, instead of mechanical, power to move loads. Big motors and their electric supplies will become more compact and precise and able to mimic small movements, such as those carried out by the muscles of the human hand. The automotive industry will lead these asset design changes. We will see electric actuators replacing steel camshafts on valved engines. Silicon and electric power will eventually knock out the entire gearbox, driveshaft, differential, and related hardware. Electric drives will direct power and turn the wheels. The overall effect will be less mechanical moving parts (and as a result less wear and tear), higher efficiency, lower energy costs and higher asset reliability. Mechanical engineering dominated the past two centuries; now we are on the threshold of seeing electrical engineering lead the way for the next century. This will happen not because we have learned how to generate light-speed electrical power but because we have finally learned how to control it.

(3) *Nanotechnology*—Nanotechnology research has focused primarily on molecular manufacturing: the creation of tools, materials, and machines that may enable us to construct the fundamental building blocks of nature easily and inexpensively. Advances in material design based on this new engineering field will revolutionize the materials available for asset design, allowing for lighter, stronger, more durable materials. The net result will be slower natu-

ral deterioration rates and fewer failures due to overloading, which will translate directly into a lower overall cost of ownership from improved energy efficiency and asset reliability.

(4) *Technology changes:*

(a) *Wireless Communication*—Improvements in wireless technology will enable handheld devices to communicate with microprocessors in critical assets.

(b) *Internet*—The Internet will continue to revolutionize how software is deployed and accessed and at the same time furnish key links to valuable information sites necessary to support effective work management. The Internet will also be the method of choice for delivering software and upgrades from the vendor.

(c) *Moore's law*—Computing power (CPU processing speed) will grow exponentially, as defined by Moore's law. As computers become faster and able to process more complex algorithms, so too will CWMS software become more complex, in terms of the computations it can carry out.

(d) *Data storage capacity*—Cheap and large volumes of storage space will expedite the capture and storage of much more data than what is possible today.

(e) *Miniaturization*—Miniaturization of hardware will result in complete business applications (e.g., computerized work management systems) operating on hand held devices, allowing realistic use of the software to support field staff.

(f) *Voice Recognition*—Voice recognition will change how data is entered.

(g) *Radio Frequency Identification (RFID)*—It has been said that RFID tags are like digital detectives that can pick you out of a crowd and monitor what you buy. This technology is an evolutionary outgrowth of the barcode. It broadcasts information continuously instead of waiting to be scanned manually. It will revolutionize the way inventory is managed, making it easy to identify and track every item that has an RFID tag. The technology will be applied to tagging of assets and will be a key enabler of the smart control systems discussed above. The tags are no bigger than a finger nail, and simpler ones hold just the model or serial number information. When a nearby scanner's transmission hits the chip, the tag's electronics are activated and the chip broadcasts its data. The more complex RFID tags will have the biggest impact on asset management. These will be able to both read and write data when communicating to another computer, such as a scanner or PDA.

(5) *Workforce changes*

    (a) *Diversity*—The make up of the work force in most first-world countries is changing dramatically as a result of immigration. This trend will continue as long as these countries need to look outside to keep its population from declining and people from third world continue to seek a better quality of life. The impact of this trend on people effectiveness will be enormous, as companies struggle to deal with different education systems, languages, culture, and skill training. Businesses have to be proactive in developing training programs to integrate these new workers into the company's culture and way of working as quickly as possible. Many companies will find they have to offer English as Second Language (ESL) programs, to get immigrants workers up to speed on company practices. This will be important in ensuring that everyone is competent in executing their roles and responsibilities around the asset lifecycle.

    (b) *Retirement of the Baby Boomers*—When employees born between 1945 and 1960 retire, companies can be drained of skilled and experienced workers. This brings with it two major challenges: vacancies in critical areas of the organization and loss of corporate knowledge. To manage these trends companies must design and implement a succession planning strategy and knowledge management practice. These two components are critical to ensuring that the right human resources are available with the right knowledge to manage the company's assets.

    (c) *Knowledge worker*—The generation that will be entering the workforce in the future will be conditioned to expect at their finger tips all the data they need to do their jobs, regardless of where they are. They are growing up in a world of hand held games and cell phones that transmit voice, text, and pictures instantaneously. Future asset management programs must leverage technology assets to meet the needs of the new generation of workers.

    (d) *Computer literacy*—As the current generation grows up with technology and computers as a part of daily life, employees will be able to deal with more complex software programs. The focus on balanced lifestyles will see a reduction in work hours and consequently less and less time on site and around the assets. There will thus be an increased dependency on off-shift and off-hours support for operations. The Integrated Technology Asset Solution will step in to fill this need through wireless communication of alarms, faults, and any other critical problems to the standby or responsible personnel. Seamless integration with process control and SCADA will provide a first line of defense remotely. If it is necessary to make a visit to the asset, the CWMS will enable the worker to properly plan the work so that site time and asset down time are minimal.

(e) *Competitive service delivery*—Competitive services are a trend for which public enterprises have to prepare. Customers will quickly find themselves unable to support additional rate increases and taxes to meet new asset management needs. The governing groups (city councils etc.) and plant management could find themselves out of a job, if customers perceive mismanagement of their investment in the municipality's asset infrastructure. The people responsible for taking care of the assets and providing services will have to look at competitive service delivery models to keep costs in line and maximize returns on the assets. These models will provide direction and guidance on the best mix of internal and external resources and the best ownership model for assets. It is very likely that the concepts of Design Build Operate and Public Private Partnerships will become the asset ownership models of choice in the public realm.

(f) *Supervision to leadership*—Many organizational designs will embody the change from supervision to leadership of teams. Middle managers will find that empowered team members prefer mentoring, coaching, guidance, and conflict/issue resolution from their leader rather that the micro-management associated with the traditional approach to managing staff. Indeed, middle managers will find they are able to create more value for the organization by empowering team members to bring out the best in them, by actively looking for ways to help them work smarter and be successful, and by focusing on medium-term planning for their business unit or group.

(g) *Innovation and creativity*—Many companies will find they can create tremendous value internally by forming a continuous improvement business unit and giving the staff in the unit adequate support to carry out its responsibilities.

(6) *Practices related changes*

Budgetary pressures will force companies to continually search for ways to maximize productivity of resources.

    (a) *Process mapping and improvement*—There will be ongoing review of business processes with the basic objective of identifying redundancy and non-value added tasks. Rapid changes in technology, asset design, people skills, and expertise will force companies to re-examine their business processes regularly to see if things can be done differently and less expensively.

    (b) *Continuous improvement*—Six sigma, lean manufacturing, total quality management, total productive maintenance will all be applied in various ways to instill a culture of continuous improvement in the workforce.

    (c) *Operational practices*—Operators will find themselves moving out of the control room and doing more operational tasks, as the control room itself becomes mobile through advances in the use of PDAs, wireless technology and automation and control.

    (d) *Maintenance practices*—Maintenance will move from the proactive to the optimized realm, where most of the work done on assets will be predictive in nature (over 60% of PMs) with a focus on knowing where each asset is on its deterioration curve at any point in time. This practice will be fully enabled by the ITS for collecting and analyzing asset date on a real-time basis and executing corrective decisions using the CWMS component of the ITS.

    (e) *Support services*— Groups such as engineering, finance, materials management, human resources, and information technology will all genuinely understand and accept their role of being service providers to internal clients, as they all focus on the common objective of maximizing asset return through lowest overall cost of ownership.

Many of the above ideas and concepts are on the radar of progressive companies, which are actively developing strategies to embrace them and ensure they achieve the difficult goal of sustainability. You can also incorporate these ideas and concepts into your strategic planning process and continuously make changes to your asset management program, so that your company can also be sustainable. As each year goes by, there will be new discoveries, innovative technological breakthroughs, advances in people effectiveness concepts and many more changes. As a result, your asset management program must be updated on an ongoing basis to ensure survival, profitability and a high-performance organization.

REFERENCES

1. *Computerized Work Management Systems for Utilities and Plant Operations,* Roopchan Lutchman, 2005.
2. *Mechanical Engineering Magazine,* May 2005.

INTRODUCTION

Asset management as a complete program is still in its infancy. The municipal sector (public works, water, and wastewater) in Australia and New Zealand is held up by many as the leader in the design and implementation of an asset management as a full program. In fact, companies are trying to develop and implement programs that are exactly like those in Australia and New Zealand. It seems, however, that the focus has been mainly on the "Strategy" and "Asset" pieces of the puzzle instead of all four elements that we have discussed so far.

Asset management is good for business and could improve almost any company. It is, however, necessary to recognize how it would work in your operating context and whether you are already practicing some of the elements of asset management. As we have seen in the preceding chapters, numerous components of asset management may already be in place in all industry sectors.

There are two key aspects of asset management that must be considered when you evaluate if your company is doing asset management. The first focuses on the right balance of the asset, people, and business process components around the lifecycle of different assets for minimizing the overall cost of ownership, maximizing reliability, and meeting the performance standards of the assets. The second focuses on the sustainability of the organization and whether the key asset management elements related to this important objective are in place. The following case studies exemplify three kinds of companies: those who have formally adopted asset management, those practicing some form of asset management, and those which are too busy trying to survive and are unaware of, or unable to adopt, asset management best practices. The case studies are based on the author's experience over the last 24 years in utilities (water, wastewater and electric, oil and gas), and manufacturing.

CASE STUDY # 1—WATER OPERATIONS

Water is a precious commodity all over the world, and the municipalities in southern California are acutely aware of the importance of managing their water resources in a responsible manner. The present case pertains to one water district's strategy to meet its growing water needs in a balanced manner, focusing on sustainability, e.g., economics, the environment, and its social responsibilities. The District chose sustainability as its theme and sought to solve its challenges through a sustainable asset management approach. This is a good example of a company practicing the fundamentals of asset management in planning for a major new asset investment. The District is investing in a new water treatment plant for treating wastewater and re-injecting it into potable water aquifers. The design is based on a sound business case, which considers demand/supply side analysis resulting in new assets (based on use of new technology) and upgrades of existing infrastructure. The re-use of the wastewater effluent was stimulated in part by a deep concern for the environment. The District has also invested a lot of time and money in ensuring that the citizens are aware of the project and has incorporated their concerns into the planning and design process.

The focus of the new water plant project is on the three elements of asset management—assets, people, and processes.

Assets—the plant design is based on leading-edge water treatment and asset design technologies to guarantee plant performance (both quality and throughput). The District has recognized the importance of doing a good job up front in the design, creation, and commissioning phases of the asset lifecycle, which in turn gives the operations and maintenance staff the best opportunity to meet the desired service levels and asset reliability targets. In addition to creating the most appropriate asset mix to deliver their vision and mission for water services, the District has also invested wisely in technology assets to enable the various work practices associated with taking care of the assets. An integrated technology asset solution comprising Financial Information System (FIS), Enterprise Asset Management System (EAMS) and Process Control System (PCS) is scheduled to go live at the same time that the plant is commissioned.

People—In recognizing that people are critical to the success of the project and to achieving maximum return on investment, a full staffing analysis was conducted. The analysis allowed the District to determine the best design, roles, responsibilities, skills/competencies, and staffing numbers necessary to effectively operate and maintain the plant. The skills development to achieve this goal has been identified and will be delivered as part of a focused training program for operations and maintenance of the assets as well as use of the technology solution necessary to execute the various business processes. The goal here is ongoing knowledge transfer to staff as the project progresses.

Processes—All critical business processes have been identified, and the various strategies are being developed. The District is partnering with asset and maintenance management experts to ensure that these concepts are well understood by staff and will be incorporated into the overall design. For example, assets are being evaluated based on criticality, and maintenance plans are being drawn up for every maintainable asset. All assets will then be set up in the EAMS with appropriate data (specifications, operations and maintenance plans, drawings etc.). During commissioning, all key data to track the health of critical assets will be captured to form a baseline for ongoing comparison, as the asset is used up in service delivery. The goal for all business processes is minimum overall cost of ownership through maximum reliability, while meeting performance standards.

The District in question has embarked on an ambitious program and is well on the way to adding a major asset to its operations. The added asset will be sustainable for this generation and that to come.

CASE STUDY # 2—OIL AND GAS

The second case focuses on the oil and gas industry. In this industry there is a clear and observable relationship between the reliability and performance of the assets and revenue. Every hour of down time can be equated to loss in revenue as a result of reduced oil or gas throughput. With demand for oil rising constantly, producers are acutely aware of the importance of effective asset management. In addition, asset breakdown in the offshore environment can also be a direct threat to the environment through spills and leaks.

Assets—The company in this case has over 30 offshore structures ranging from very large manned platforms to a number of smaller clusters, production manifolds, etc. The average age of the structures is 20 to 30 years. In an offshore hostile environment this means that most of these assets are nearing the end of their overall lifecycle. The oil and natural gas fields are mature, which means that most production is through secondary recovery (gas and water injection, hydraulic and electric submersible pumps). Secondary recovery has introduced much more complexity into the asset mix and thus more challenges for the O&M staff. Support assets are also a key part of the asset mix, with a number of offshore electricity generating stations, boats to transport staff to and from the platforms, as well as crane barges and other ancillary equipment. There is an aggressive capital program to find new fields and install new assets to keep production at targeted levels. There is no formal asset management program in place and asset management is considered to be making the best use of the CMMS. Supply and demand side modeling is not actively practiced. Little economic justification is offered for the upgrade/modifications aspect of the capital projects program. In fact, the argument is presented that it is more economical and profitable for the company to shut down a number of the smaller producers instead of spending the money to refurbish these structures. Another challenge on the asset front is the level of use of technology assets—which is limited to standalone business applications and is generally used as a repository of data only after transactions are done. The Finance and Administration department has selected an Enterprise Resource Planning system (ERP) to manage their finance, human resources, and materials management business processes. As an afterthought, it was decided to make use of the plant maintenance module of the ERP. There is a current initiative in place to configure and deploy this module for use by maintenance staff. Progress is slow and buy-in from end users is very low. Many feel that the module does not meet their needs and think that the IT specialists just want to complete the project and claim victory.

People—The company in the past has experimented with various organizational designs and has moved to the concept of geographical teams responsible for similar assets and production targets. Unfortunately, they have chosen to become fully decentralized in the area of maintenance. This has resulted in widespread duplication of effort and poor utilization of resources. In addition, knowledge sharing has been restricted to the various teams, and very little learning is shared across teams. The company has a militant union. Negotiations are hard fought battles resulting in increased salaries, additional job classifications, and policies that inhibit innovation and creativity. The management structure is autocratic—with numerous layers, which does not help the union/management relationship. The concept of empowered teams is an elusive goal for this company. The balanced score card approach to performance management is being practiced at the corporate level but has not trickled down to the frontline teams doing the actual work

Processes—Business processes are focused more on control rather then effectiveness. An enterprise resource system has been implemented to manage the financial, materials management, and human resources processes. The current push is for maintenance to utilize the plant maintenance module to support the preventive maintenance program. PM in the system is simplistic, time-based, reserved for critical assets. Some attempt has been made to implement predictive maintenance in the form of oil and vibration analysis. The success of this program has not been evaluated. The concept of planning and scheduling with associated metrics (e.g., WR/WO backlog, PM, and schedule compliance) are not in place. Another group that decides what is right for the maintenance group is currently implementing reliability-centered maintenance pilots.

This company is profitable at this time because of the high demand and price for its products. It obvious that the current approach to all three components of asset management is not fully understood or well practiced. Sustainability and in fact long- term survival are open to question. A firm such as this could benefit from the ideas and concepts of sustainable asset management.

CASE STUDY # 3—PUBLIC WORKS

The third case study exemplifies how asset management can become out of balance when the asset mix is not matched to business drivers. In question is a public works utility responsible for the roads, parks, recreational facilities, and storm/sewer system for a large North American city. In the past the city was home to large industries and to people looking for gainful employment. In response to population growth the city invested in new roads, underground pipes, water/wastewater plants and recreational facilities. Over the last five to ten years the city experienced a loss of industries and population. Capital and operating funds have shrunk, and it is difficult to generate new money through rate increases and additional taxes.

Assets—This municipality has a large asset infrastructure to be maintained with dwindling budgets. There is an asset condition deficit, and authorities would like to bring assets back up to acceptable conditions. Assets are generally being used at levels of performance below design levels and, as a result, are being used inefficiently (in the areas of labor, energy, use of operating supplies etc.). For example, the city continues to maintain a number of fully staffed recreational facilities with only a 30--40% usage by citizens. Similarly, buildings and treatment facilities are under-utilized. A proper demand and supply side analysis and scenario modeling would be very useful in consolidating assets and possibly decommissioning those that are no longer necessary. This might lead to better use of labor and material resources, reduced energy consumption, and increase service levels where they are most needed. The department also faces another asset-related challenge—technology assets. Most of the business applications are standalone, and current applications seem to have been designed to meet the needs of the corporate groups (e.g., finance) instead of the end-users. The city should actively pursue the development of an integrated technology asset master plan with the objective of selecting and implementing the most suitable enabling technologies to help frontline teams be more effective at their jobs.

People—As in many municipalities, the city's Public Works Department is one of many different groups that work in isolation. In addition, there are divisions within the department that also tend to focus solely on their roles and responsibilities. Coordination around the asset lifecycle is therefore a challenge, and many decisions are sub-optimal because of this inefficiency. The department is also faced with the additional challenge of baby boomer retirements. While this helps with staffing reductions, it also poses problems for corporate knowledge retention. The leadership style is bureaucratic (in fact, some think it is autocratic), and communication is top down. This has resulted in staff taking a "wait-to-be told" attitude. As you would expect, the labor and management relationship is adversarial, and it is a daily challenge for middle management who find themselves trying to deal with senior management's directives and motivate frontline employees to be more effective at their jobs. Most of the know-how necessary for staff to be effective at delivering the required services is not available in electronic knowledge bases. It resides in the heads of potential retirees. The people effectiveness strategies discussed in this book provide guidelines for dealing with these challenges.

Processes—In the city's O&M area, the work environment is very reactive. Work planning and scheduling are simple or non-existent. The CMMS is a repository (after the fact) of work done by staff, and the data is not actively used to drive proactive decisions. Materials management is a challenge with respect to the proper balance of stock and not- stock purchases. O&M staff have minimal involvement in the capital projects process and have issues with projects that are handed over to them in the areas of maintainability, interchangeability of components, and overall documentation (specifications, drawings, bill of materials and maintenance plans). Pressure is ongoing to reduce O&M budgets and maintain the same level of service. The result is a daily challenge for operators to deliver services to meet customer expectations and an ongoing grind for maintenance who keep putting out fires. The business processes concepts discussed in this book would be useful to this company. The results would be even more impressive if business processes were implemented together with the suggestions for the assets and people elements.

CASE STUDY # 4—MANUFACTURING

Case study # 4 involves a North American steel company that has been in the foundry and downstream steel products business for nearly 100 years. The company supplies the automotive business and users of rods and wire component. Over the last decade the steel industry has been hit hard by increasing energy costs and global competition. The U.S. and Canadian governments have tried to help these industries through trade tariffs, anti-dumping regulations, and incentives, which are intended to give these companies time to find innovative ways to be competitive and sustain their businesses. It has been a tough journey, in the face of unrelenting competition from Asian suppliers. Our case study subject has struggled with the challenge of competitiveness and sustainability. At the time of writing of this book, the company has been the target of acquisition by other companies; there is general disenchantment by shareholders and a belief in some quarters that the company is headed for bankruptcy.

Assets—The vicious cycle of poor profits and fewer funds for capital projects has limited the company's ability to invest in technologically advanced asserts. The net result is a higher overall cost of production and inability to meet production targets at times. In addition, the company has found it difficult to make the investments to meet the changing needs of its customers for more specialized products.

People—The management structure is very traditional and the leadership style is considered to be autocratic. Communication is top down, and the management- employee relationship lacks trust. The strong union environment has inhibited multi-skilling, workforce flexibility, performance management, and empowered team concepts. The situation is further compromised by an adversarial union unwilling to budge on the need to reduce compensation and benefits, which is claimed to be a vital requirement to survival of the company. A great deal of work must be done to achieve the level of people effectiveness discussed in the book. Management and the union have to understand that the survival of the company and the future of all employees rest on a partnership approach to implementing the concepts necessary for organizational effectiveness.

Processes—Limited funds for maintenance have resulted in a reactive work environment where putting out fires is the order of the day. Optimized maintenance concepts are not fully understood or practiced by the maintenance staff. Materials management is an ongoing challenge of trying to find spare parts for obsolete assets. In fact, many spare parts have to be manufactured by special order, since the OEMs are no longer in business or do not carry the spares anymore. Coordination of business processes across the asset lifecycle is not well executed. In addition, the company has recently embarked on an initiative to improve work management by implementing a CMMS. The implementation team has been going it alone and has been struggling to configure the software, populate the database, and make the software available to the maintenance staff.

Their neighbor (and competitor), facing the same challenges, has been widely successful in reinventing its business and competing successfully in the market. They have applied sustainable asset management practices to go beyond survival. They have invested in highly automated, energy-efficient assets that create specialized products to fill niche markets. Similarly, they have re-designed business processes and embarked on optimized maintenance concepts (the right mix of reactive and proactive tactics), continuously seeking to maximize asset reliability and minimize overall cost of ownership. Their efforts at improving people effectiveness have paid big returns in terms of superior leadership, team dynamics, workforce flexibility, performance management, and entrepreneurship.

The first company can restore control, competitiveness, and ultimately establish sustainability only if they apply the concepts discussed in this book, thus learning from the experiences and successes of their neighbor.

"As Is" work processes—documentation of the existing work processes in your operations as part of the reengineering process

Asset—entity that can be used to meet the needs of a client or customer by: performing an operation, functioning as part of a process, producing a product or performing a service

Asset Life Cycle—the nine phases of the life of an asset capturing the type of work done on the asset from creation to decommissioning

Asset Management—the optimization of the life cycle of an asset to meet performance standards in a safe and environmentally sound manner through smart: Planning, Investment, Financing, Engineering, Operations, Maintenance, Refurbishment and Replacement

Asset Management Index—overall index on performance in the asset management areas based on an asset management review around the asset life cycle

Asset Management System—a business application that allows users to set up assets in an asset registry, plot deterioration curves and provide guidance on upgrade, modification and replacement type decisions

BOM (Bill of Materials)—listing of spare parts needed to maintain the asset

BOH (Balance on Hand)—quantity of stock item in the warehouse, this is a dynamic number and changes based on inventory transactions

CAE—computer aided design, a design practice that leverages technology to maximize design and testing of components or complete products prior to creation of the physical product

CCTV—Closed Circuit Television, used to inspect sewer lines etc.

CBM—condition based monitoring to track and monitor the health of assets in a proactive manner (used interchangeably with PdM—predictive maintenance).

CIP—capital improvement program (for new assets or upgrade, modification and replacement of existing assets

CLAIR—Cleaning, Lubricating, Adjustment, Inspection and Repair type work done by operators in a Total Productive Maintenance environment

CMOM—Capacity Management Operations and Maintenance regulation in the USA focused on improving accountability and stewardship of the sewers and storm sewer assets in municipalities

CPU—central processing unit of a computer

CRP (Conference Room Pilot)—software implementation phase dedicated to training of the core team, loading of test data, configuration and testing of the system

CRM—Customer Resource Management system, a business application that captures and tracks customer related data aimed at providing information to maximize customer satisfaction

CWMS (Computerized Work Management System)—software used to execute work management and related transactions and at the same time store data needed to support work and cost history

DBO—Design-Build-Operate, an asset creation, operation and maintenance option that is used when the company does not what to be burdened with the challenges associated with operating and maintaining the assets

EAMS (Enterprise Asset Management System)—same definition as CWMS but with an additional focus on functionality aimed at asset condition tracking and extending asset reliability

EDMS (Electronic Document Management System)—software used to electronically store and manage documents in a secure environment

ERP—Enterprise Resources Planning system, a business application that tries to provide a one-stop solution to technology needs: financials, human resources, production/operations management, customer order taking, maintenance management and materials management

Earned Value—Project management measure: Cost of actual work accomplished/Cost of planned work for the period

FIS—Financial Information System, a business application that enables key financial business process e.g. accounts receivables, accounts payables, budgeting, check reconciliation, purchasing etc.

GASB 34—Government Standards and Accounting Board of the USA, regulation 34 focused on asset reporting to demonstrate accountability and stewardship of public infrastructure

GIS—Geographical Information Systems (a computer business application that provides a view of assets based on maps)

Interface—software programs that link different business software allowing the timely exchange of information needed to support various business processes

ITS—integrated technology solution that is the linked business applications, operating system, databases, hardware and networking systems needed to enable the various business processes around the asset life cycle

JIT (Just In Time)—refers to materials management (inventory and purchasing) arrangements that ensures any materials or services are there just in time to support the work and operations processes (usually the responsibility for JIT is placed on the vendor with appropriate terms and conditions)

LAN (Local Area Network)—network infrastructure or servers, computers, terminals, interconnecting cables, printers and other peripheral devices local to a plant or facility

Lean Manufacturing—the relentless pursuit of the elimination of waste in manufacturing operation

LIMS—Laboratory Information Systems, a business application that enables the various laboratory processes e.g. sampling management, storage of test results, preparation of reports, tracking of regulations and test procedures etc.

MRO Spares (Maintenance, Repairs and Overhaul Spares)—used in the support of the work management process (items usually stocked in the warehouse)

MSDS—Material Safety Data Sheet, provides key safety information on materials (stocked or direct purchase) for storage and handling

MTBF—Mean Time Between Failure (measure of asset reliability)

MTTR—Mean Time To Repair (measure of maintainability)

Nessie Curve—term used to refer to the curves on the financial projections graph for asset replacement

NPV (Net Present Value)—a financial indicator derived from a business case evaluation used to determine the attractiveness of a project. NPV considers the time value of money and calculates (based on an assumed interest rate) what the overall cost and investment dollars would be in each year of the project

Overall Equipment Efficiency—popular measure of asset performance and is a function of: Quality × Rate × Efficiency

Optimized Work (or Optimized Maintenance)—optimal mix of proactive and reactive work and the optimal mix of predictive maintenance based on reliability centered maintenance evaluations

P3—Public- Private-Partnerships, an alternative approach to funding and managing public assets

PBP (Pay Back Period)—this is another indicator of project economic feasibility and is the year that cumulative expenditure is equal to the cumulative savings, any time after this point you can expect some return on the investment

PdM—predictive maintenance to track, monitor and manage the health of assets in a proactive manner (used interchangeably with CBM—condition based maintenance)

P&ID—Process and Instrumentation Drawings

PM (Preventive Maintenance)—work or maintenance tasks based on a set frequency or statistic aimed at arresting or eliminating deterioration of an asset or rebuilding back to its original condition e.g. lubrication and overhauls

PIR (Post Implementation Review)—this is the last phase of the software implementation process and allows for a complete review of the software in use by end users and sets the stage for modifications or changes (of organization, practices and technology components) in order to maximize the benefits from the investment

Proactive Work (or Proactive Maintenance)—maintenance or work done in advance of asset failure, proactive work is always planned

Reactive Work (or Reactive Maintenance)—maintenance or work done after asset failure. Emergency type work is the only type of reactive work that is not planned. All other reactive work should be planned.

Reliability—an indication of the average time an asset can operate with out failing (Mean Time Before Failure is the most common measure of reliability)

RCM, Reliability Centered Maintenance—a scientific step-by-step approach to developing maintenance plans for an asset by determining all the various functions, failure modes, consequences combinations and determining the best approach to taking care of the asset

RFI—Request For Information (purchasing tool used to explore the options available in the market place)

RFID—Radio Frequency IDentification, computer technology that replaces the barcode for tracking and monitoring parts and assets

RFP—Request For Proposal (purchasing tool used to seek proposal responses from qualified candidates in the market place)

ROI (Rate of Return)—this is another indicator of project economic feasibility and is the interest rate that makes the overall NPV equal to zero

RONA—return on net assets, a measure of the financial returns on the investment in the asset infrastructure

ROP (Re-Order Point)—this is the minimum stock item balance on hand at which reordering of the item (automatically in the CWMS or manually) is necessary in order to maintain acceptable stores service level for the item.

ROQ (Re Order Quantity)—minimum order quantity purchased when the item reaches the reorder point

SCADA (Supervisory Control And Data Acquisition)—business software the enables automation of assets or groups of assets in a plant, operators can remotely operate and manage these assets by sending commands from a computer screen

SDLC (System Development Life Cycle)—a proven method to proactively manage an integrated technology solution in a world of continuously changing technology

SLA (Service Level Agreements)—internal contracts between organizational groups that sets standards of performance

Six-Sigma (6σ)—this is a quality improvement methodology that pursues a goal of near-perfection in meeting customer requirements by achieving 3.4 parts per million potential defects

SOP (Standard Operating Procedure)—standard procedures for operating or maintaining an asset

SWOT—Strengths, Weaknesses, Opportunities and Threats, a strategic high level analysis on the attractiveness of a project

"To Be" work processes—documentation of the new way of working by applying best in class concepts to your existing to eliminate non-value added and redundant activities

TPM—Total Productive Maintenance, operators trained and certified competent in doing Cleaning, Lubricating, Adjustment, Inspection and Repair (CLAIR) type work allowing the maintenance trades top focus on more core and complex maintenance tasks

WAN (Wide Area Network)—network of LANs through interconnecting cable (fiber optics) or through wireless communication

WBS—Work, Breakdown Structures, logical packages of related work in a project plan or schedule

Work Management Process—refers to the seven step work process common to any work situation—initiation, planning, scheduling, execution, closeout, history and evaluation